The State of
Butterflies
in Britain and Ireland

Richard Fox, Jim Asher, Tom Brereton, David Roy and Martin Warren

Butterfly Conservation

Centre for Ecology and Hydrology

The Dublin Naturalists' Field Club

piscespublications

Dedicated to the many butterfly recorders, past and present,
whose magnificent efforts have made it possible to assess
the state of our butterflies in such detail.

We would also like to thank our wives/partners:
Tamsin, Denise, Paula, Helen and Dee, for all of their support
and great patience during another five years of butterfly
recording and monitoring.

First published 2006 by Pisces Publications for Butterfly Conservation.
Pisces Publications is the imprint of NatureBureau.

British Library-in-Publication Data
A catalogue record of this book is available from the British Library.

ISBN 1 874357 31 5

Designed and produced by NatureBureau, 36 Kingfisher Court, Hambridge Road, Newbury, Berkshire RG14 5SJ
www.naturebureau.co.uk

Printed by Information Press, Oxford

Contents

Foreword

This is an important book that charts the fortunes of butterflies at the start of the twenty-first century. It not only demonstrates that butterflies are sensitive indicators of the health of our countryside and of the impact of human activity on the environment, but also highlights the enormous and vital contribution that volunteers make towards our understanding of the natural world.

The contents are alarming. They show that the distributions and populations of many butterflies continue to decline. However, there is cause for some optimism. A few of our most threatened species have bucked the trend and are showing promising signs of recovery. The role of Butterfly Conservation and its conservation partners in these successes has been crucial. I am particularly heartened to hear of the success of the globally endangered Large Blue butterfly following its careful reintroduction and of the re-expansion of the Silver-spotted Skipper and Adonis Blue, in part due to the restoration of appropriate grazing regimes on our downland.

The loss of biodiversity is one of the biggest environmental problems facing the planet. As part of its international commitments, the UK Government has set itself the challenging target of halting the loss of biodiversity by 2010. This book shows how we might achieve this for some of our most demanding species.

The book also documents the profound effect that climate change is having on our butterflies and how this is bringing new challenges to the conservation of our biodiversity. Butterflies provide an important way of monitoring and predicting how these new threats will affect our wildlife in the coming decades.

I am therefore delighted with the formation of the new, greatly enlarged, UK Butterfly Monitoring Scheme co-ordinated by Butterfly Conservation, the Centre of Ecology and Hydrology, and the Joint Nature Conservation Committee. This is the largest scheme of its kind anywhere in the world. It will develop the valuable role of butterflies as indicators and provide a litmus test of future government policy impacts on the environment, especially the new agri-environment schemes that have been designed to reverse the decline of farmland biodiversity.

We must, however, conserve butterflies in their own right. They are beautiful and emblematic species and part of our own quality of life.

Jim Knight MP
UK Minister for Biodiversity and Rural Affairs

Preface

We live in a time of rapid, perhaps unprecedented, environmental change. As a result our biodiversity is changing too. Continued fragmentation, deterioration and loss of wildlife habitats, pollution, and the accelerating rate of climate change pose considerable challenges for many species, as well as providing opportunities for others. Butterflies have been shown to be very sensitive to these changes, and have fared worse than birds and vascular plants in Britain over recent decades. There is a greater need than ever to track changes in our butterfly fauna. Recording and monitoring provide the foundation for effective conservation of threatened butterfly species, but they also indicate the changing fortunes of thousands of other insect species.

The Butterflies for the New Millennium (BNM) project was set up in the early 1990s to understand, in detail, the distribution of butterflies across Britain and Ireland and to track changes in these distributions. The results of the intensive BNM survey carried out between 1995 and 1999 were published in 2001 in *The Millennium Atlas of Butterflies in Britain and Ireland*. This landmark publication, which has sold over 10,000 copies, provided a much-needed reference for naturalists and ecologists on the state of knowledge about butterflies at that time, and how they had fared since the first major survey (1970–82).

In parallel with distribution recording, transect monitoring over the past thirty years has provided a great wealth of information on the ecology and population status of butterflies, and on the effects of habitat management, land management policies and climate change. Monitoring began in 1976 with the establishment of the Butterfly Monitoring Scheme, which enjoys an international reputation for the quality of its scientific outputs. Transect walking has proved an incredibly popular activity amongst recorders, leading to hundreds of independent transects being established. These have been co-ordinated by Butterfly Conservation since the late 1990s. The newly formed UK Butterfly Monitoring Scheme (UKBMS), co-ordinated by the Centre for Ecology and Hydrology, Butterfly Conservation and the Joint Nature Conservation Committee, brings all these data together for the first time, into one of the largest annual monitoring schemes for insect populations in the world.

The Millennium Atlas, along with transect monitoring and subsequent research utilising the underlying data, revealed startlingly rapid rates of distribution and population change amongst Britain and Ireland's butterflies. Many species had declined rapidly, but a significant minority had increased dramatically. This picture of radical change confirmed the need to maintain the momentum of the BNM and transect monitoring schemes, and lent support to the idea of five-year atlas updates.

This publication represents the first such update and the first assessment of the state of Britain and Ireland's butterflies in the twenty-first century. It reports on a further five-year period of distribution recording, based on the same approach as was used for *The Millennium Atlas*. Over 1.6 million new butterfly records have been collated by the BNM project for 2000–04. This matches the number collated for 1995–99, and brings the total BNM database to about 4.5 million butterfly records. Analysis of this powerful and up-to-date source of information is complemented by new population trends from monitoring at over 1,000 sites in the UKBMS data set. This resource represents an incredible 140,801 separate visits by highly skilled recorders who have walked over 350,000km (almost as far as the moon is from the earth!) and counted more than 10.5 million individual butterflies.

The updated distribution maps, population-level plots and trends resulting from analysis of these new data show further changes in distribution and abundance, and provide an essential and contemporary reference for the state of our butterfly fauna. A detailed interpretation of the results provides important implications for conservation and land-use policies and the potential future impacts of climate change.

In the foreword to *The Millennium Atlas*, Sir David Attenborough, President of Butterfly Conservation, wrote of butterflies that: 'Like miners' canaries they can give warnings of environmental dangers'. The updated results reported here indicate that his analogy remains every bit as compelling as it did in 2001.

This book is a further tribute to the many thousands of volunteer recorders who, through their extraordinary efforts both in the field and in front of the computer, compiled the impressive and important volume of data for both BNM and UKBMS projects. Without their vital input, this assessment of our wonderful butterflies would simply not be possible. We, and everyone who makes use of these results, are deeply indebted to these recorders.

Richard Fox
Jim Asher
Tom Brereton
David Roy
Martin Warren

Acknowledgements

The State of Butterflies in Britain and Ireland

Many people have contributed towards the text contained in this book, particularly the local co-ordinators listed opposite. We are extremely grateful to them and to the following colleagues who also commented on text or provided information: Bob Aldwell, Andy Barker, Ken Bond, Nigel Bourn, Caroline Bulman, Andy Butler, Peter Carvill, John Davis, Jane Ellis, Sam Ellis, Keith Futter, Chris Gardiner, Sharon Hearle, Jane Hill, Dan Hoare, Russel Hobson, Stuart Hodges, Maurice Hughes, David Jackson, Gail Jeffcoate, Stephen Jeffcoate, Jenny Joy, Paul Kirkland, Ian McLean, Jon Mercer, David Nash, Steve Nash, Roger Norman, Matthew Oates, Colin Pope, Barry Prater, Tom Prescott, Andrew Pullin, Dave Simcox, Mike Slater, Chris Thomas, Jeremy Thomas, Tom Wigglesworth and Mike Williams.

Roger Dennis proof-read the manuscript and we are very grateful to him for his many helpful comments.

Information used to map the location of Réal's Wood White and Wood White records in Ireland (shown in the Réal's Wood White species account) was kindly provided by Maurice Hughes (Butterfly Conservation), Brian Nelson (Ulster Museum), Ken Bond (University College Cork) and Jim Whitehouse.

Photographs and illustrations

Jim Asher, Tom Brereton, Peter Eeles, Richard Lewington, Paul Pugh, Jeremy Thomas and Robert Thompson.

Front cover: Pearl-bordered Fritillary ©Jim Asher
Title page: Silver-studded Blues ©Richard Lewington
p.3: Volunteer walking a transect ©Tom Brereton
p.17: Chequered Skipper ©Jim Asher
p.18: Small Skipper ©Jim Asher
p.19: Essex Skipper ©Paul Pugh
p.20: Lulworth Skipper ©Paul Pugh
p.21: Silver-spotted Skipper ©Jim Asher
p.22: Large Skipper ©Jim Asher
p.23: Dingy Skipper ©Jim Asher
p.24: Grizzled Skipper ©Tom Brereton
p.25: Swallowtail ©Robert Thompson
p.26: Wood White ©Jim Asher
p.27: Réal's Wood White ©Robert Thompson
p.28: Clouded Yellow ©Jim Asher
p.29: Brimstone ©Jim Asher
p.30: Large White ©Jim Asher
p.31: Small White ©Jim Asher
p.32: Green-veined White ©Robert Thompson
p.33: Orange-tip ©Robert Thompson
p.34: Green Hairstreak ©Jim Asher
p.35: Brown Hairstreak ©Jim Asher
p.36: Purple Hairstreak ©Robert Thompson
p.37: White-letter Hairstreak ©Robert Thompson
p.38: Black Hairstreak ©Jim Asher
p.39: Small Copper ©Jim Asher
p.40: Small Blue ©Jim Asher
p.41: Silver-studded Blue ©Tom Brereton
p.42: Brown Argus ©Jim Asher
p.43: Northern Brown Argus ©Jim Asher
p.44: Common Blue ©Jim Asher
p.45: Chalkhill Blue ©Jim Asher
p.46: Adonis Blue ©Jim Asher
p.47: Holly Blue ©Robert Thompson
p.48: Large Blue ©Jim Asher
p.49: Duke of Burgundy ©Robert Thompson
p.50: White Admiral ©Robert Thompson

p.51: Purple Emperor ©Peter Eeles
p.52: Red Admiral ©Robert Thompson
p.53: Painted Lady ©Robert Thompson
p.54: Small Tortoiseshell ©Jim Asher
p.55: Peacock ©Jim Asher
p.56: Comma ©Jim Asher
p.57: Small Pearl-bordered Fritillary ©Robert Thompson
p.58: Pearl-bordered Fritillary ©Jim Asher
p.59: High Brown Fritillary ©Jim Asher
p.60: Dark Green Fritillary ©Robert Thompson
p.61: Silver-washed Fritillary ©Robert Thompson
p.62: Marsh Fritillary ©Robert Thompson
p.63: Glanville Fritillary ©Jim Asher
p.64: Heath Fritillary ©Robert Thompson
p.65: Speckled Wood ©Jim Asher
p.66: Wall ©Robert Thompson
p.67: Mountain Ringlet ©Jim Asher
p.68: Scotch Argus ©Paul Pugh
p.69: Marbled White ©Jim Asher
p.70: Grayling ©Jim Asher
p.71: Gatekeeper ©Jim Asher
p.72: Meadow Brown ©Jim Asher
p.73: Ringlet ©Jim Asher
p.74: Small Heath ©Jim Asher
p.75: Large Heath ©Jim Asher
p.76: Queen of Spain Fritillary ©Robert Thompson
p.91: Greenham Common ©Jim Asher
p.91: Duke of Burgundy ©Robert Thompson
p.93: Fragmented landscape ©Jim Asher
p.93: Marsh Fritillary ©Robert Thompson
p.94: Large Heath ©Paul Pugh
p.95: Silver-spotted Skipper ©Jim Asher
p.97: Adonis Blue ©Jim Asher
p.99: Cattle grazing ©Tom Brereton
p.103: Large Blues mating ©Jeremy Thomas
Back cover: Pearl-bordered Fritillary ©Jim Asher

Project co-ordination and funding

We would like to thank Butterfly Conservation's Advisory Group on Lepidoptera Recording and Monitoring, a multi-organisation committee that guides this area of our work. *The State of Butterflies in Britain and Ireland* draws upon two major projects: Butterflies for the New Millennium and the UKBMS (and its predecessors the Butterfly Monitoring Scheme and Butterfly Conservation's Transect project).

Butterflies for the New Millennium is co-ordinated by Butterfly Conservation, the Dublin Naturalists' Field Club and the Biological Records Centre. Funding contributions for the project during the 2000–04 period were generously provided by the Bernard Sunley Charitable Foundation and Esmée Fairbairn Foundation. The involvement of Biological Records Centre in the project is thanks to the support of the Centre for Ecology and Hydrology (CEH) and Joint Nature Conservation Committee (JNCC). We would like to thank David Bridges for his work in raising funds for the project.

The following organisations kindly provided distribution data sets for the 2000–04 period: Butterfly Monitoring Scheme (CEH and JNCC), Centre for Ecology and Hydrology (projects: Farm Scale Evaluations (FSE) of genetically modified herbicide-tolerant crops; BUZZ (BD1624); SAFFIE (LK0926); the Manor Farm Project; the Salisbury Plain Training Area invertebrate survey), Countryside Council for Wales, Leeds University, National Garden Butterfly Survey, Scottish Natural Heritage, The Women's Institute, York University.

The UKBMS project (BD1453) supported the analyses of transect data for this book. The project is funded by a multi-agency consortium led by Defra, and including the Countryside Council for Wales, English Nature, Environment and Heritage Service, Forestry Commission, Scottish Executive Environment and Rural Affairs Department, and Scottish Natural Heritage. The Butterfly Monitoring Scheme, co-ordinated by the Centre for Ecology and Hydrology and Joint Nature Conservation Committee, and Butterfly Conservation's co-ordination of transect recording, funded by Defra (projects BD1427 and BD1446), formed the basis for the UKBMS project and collected the data used here.

We would particularly like to thank Richard Brand-Hardy (Defra), Valerie Brown (Defra), Steve Buckland (CREEM, University of St Andrews), Val Burton (CEH), Simon Gillam (Forestry Commission), Nick Greatorex-Davies (CEH), Monique MacKenzie (CREEM, University of St Andrews), Ian McLean (JNCC), Peter Rothery (CEH), Richard Seaby (Pisces Conservation), Dave Smallshire (Defra), Andy Stott (Defra), Arco van Strien (Statistics Netherlands), Chris van Swaay (Dutch Butterfly Conservation) and current and former Butterfly Conservation colleagues Rebecca Haworth, Carolyn Knight, Durwyn Liley, Poppy Mackie, Neil Sephton, Katherine Stewart and Tom Wigglesworth, for their work and advice in the development of transect data sets and analyses.

Local project co-ordination

Thousands of people and hundreds of organisations have taken part in the second five-year BNM survey and in transect recording and the authors regret that it is impossible to acknowledge them all individually. Instead, for each area that collated records or monitoring data, the local co-ordinators as at the end of 2004 are listed, together with previous co-ordinators (in brackets) who were active in the 2000–04 period.

These people, most of whom are volunteers, and the organisations that they represent, are the contact points for butterfly recording and transect monitoring across Britain and Ireland. In many cases they are ably assisted by others, too numerous to list, but for whose efforts we are extremely grateful.

BNM co-ordinators are shown in normal text, Transect co-ordinators in italics and volunteers who co-ordinate both projects in bold.

ENGLAND

Avon Bristol Regional Environmental Records Centre
Bedfordshire Keith Balmer, Peter Glenister, *Greg Herbert* (Charles Baker)
Berkshire, Buckinghamshire and Oxfordshire Jim Asher, *Mike Wilkins*
Cambridgeshire and Essex **Val Perrin**, Barry Dickerson (*Iris Newbery*)
Cheshire Barry Shaw, *Stu Burnet*
Cornwall and the Isles of Scilly John Worth, *Sally Foster*
Cumbria Stephen Hewitt, *Sarah Bradley*
Derbyshire **Ken Orpe**
Devon Roger Bristow, *Mark Ogden* (Bill Deakins)
Dorset **Bill Shreeves**, **Bernard Franklin**, **David Jeffers**, *Stephen Brown*
Gloucestershire Chris Wiltshire, *John Tilt* (Barry Embling, **Guy Meredith**)
Greater London *Leslie Williams*

Greater Manchester Peter Hardy
Hampshire and the Isle of Wight **Linda Barker**, Dave Green, *Andy Barker* (John Taverner)
Hertfordshire and north London **John Murray**, Andrew Wood, *Keir Mottram*
Kent and south-east London Mike Easterbrook, *Mike Brown* (John Maddocks)
Lancashire and Merseyside **Laura Sivell**
Leicestershire and Rutland Adrian Russell, *Ken Orpe*
Lincolnshire **Allan Binding** (*Mark Tyszka*)
Norfolk Patrick Bonham (**Brian McIlwrath**, *Colin Nicholls*)
Northamptonshire Douglas Goddard, *Greg Herbert*
Northumberland and County Durham Dave O'Brien, Mike Hunter, Roger Norman, *Brian Denham* (**Ian Waller**)
Nottinghamshire Richard Penson, *Ken Orpe* (Michael Walker)
Somerset **Mike Ridge**, **Marjorie Brunt** (Roger Sutton)
Suffolk **Rob Parker** (Richard Stewart)

Chapter 1 **Background**

Butterfly recording and monitoring

We are fortunate to have a long and popular tradition of amateur study and recording of butterflies in Britain and Ireland[1]. This tradition continues to thrive, despite many radical changes to the pattern of our lives in recent decades. *The State of Butterflies in Britain and Ireland* is the latest publication in a line stretching back to the woodcuts of Mouffet (he whose daughter 'sat on a tuffet') published in 1634 and Merrett's descriptions of British butterflies in 1666[2]. Things have changed over time, of course, and recording is now far more accurate, with sightings referenced to national mapping grids rather than the imprecision of place names. More significantly, a pioneering scheme to monitor butterfly populations was initiated across the UK during the 1970s, providing a second source of information to complement traditional distribution records.

Thanks to the skills and efforts of countless amateur and professional scientists and volunteer recorders, more is known about the butterfly fauna of Britain and Ireland than in any other region on earth. We are in a unique position to assess the changing fortunes of these beautiful and charismatic insects, and to investigate and understand the underlying causes of change, not just for butterflies but also for biodiversity as a whole. Such information is essential to conservation, ensuring that the natural heritage of Britain and Ireland, and the economic, environmental and social benefits that biodiversity brings, remain intact for future generations.

Butterflies for the New Millennium

Conservation takes place through action where species and habitats occur. Without knowing where species and habitats are, conservation is almost impossible. For this reason, distribution records are the foundation for almost all our efforts to conserve species.

Butterflies for the New Millennium (BNM) is the distribution recording scheme for butterflies in the UK, Republic of Ireland, Isle of Man and Channel Islands. It is run by Butterfly Conservation and the Dublin Naturalists' Field Club in association with the Biological Records Centre (BRC; operated by the Centre for Ecology and Hydrology and Joint Nature Conservation Committee). The backbone of the recording scheme is a network of approximately 70 local co-ordinators, volunteers and local organisations, each of which takes responsibility for the collation, verification and computerisation of butterfly distribution records in their county or wider area. Through this network, many thousands of recorders and hundreds of organisations (including local biological records centres, natural history societies and conservation organisations) volunteer their butterfly observations to the BNM scheme. Their data are used widely for biodiversity conservation, land-use planning, policy development, education, scientific research and other uses at local, national and international scales.

The BNM project was launched in 1995 and has provided the impetus for 10 years of the most intensive and comprehensive butterfly recording ever undertaken in Britain and Ireland. Data from the first five-year recording period (1995–99) were used to prepare *The Millennium Atlas of Butterflies in Britain and Ireland*, a landmark publication marking the end of the twentieth century[3]. Some 10,000 people contributed a total of 1.6 million butterfly records during this five-year period, a truly remarkable achievement.

1 Marren 1998, Salmon 2000
2 Emmet 1989
3 Asher *et al.* 2001

Despite the success of the BNM project (or perhaps because of it), some doubted that the high intensity of recording could be maintained after the publication of a high-profile atlas. However, the second five-year BNM survey (2000–04) has also been an unqualified success (see Chapter 2 for details) with recording effort and coverage maintained overall and even improved in some areas. *The State of Butterflies in Britain and Ireland* is a testament to the hard work of recorders, co-ordinators and supporters in maintaining the momentum and success of the BNM project. It provides vital feedback to encourage ongoing recording, as well as highlighting the importance of butterflies in assessing environmental change and identifying the challenges facing biodiversity conservation.

The recording since 1995 is only one facet of the BNM project. Historical (i.e. pre-1995) butterfly records have been brought together and incorporated into the BNM data set. The records gathered by BRC for the *Atlas of Butterflies in Britain and Ireland*[4] form the core of this historical resource, with a good level of national coverage for the period 1970–82 and more patchy (geographically and taxonomically) data covering the 1690–1969 and 1983–94 periods. In addition to the BRC data, BNM co-ordinators, local biological records centres and conservation bodies such as the Countryside Council for Wales, English Nature and Scottish Natural Heritage, have contributed records collected before 1995 for inclusion in the BNM data set. Some of these data have been added only recently and appear for the first time on the distribution maps in this book.

The BNM data enable the assessment of long-term trends by comparing species' distributions in different time periods. However, such trends have to be constructed and interpreted with care as the intensity and geographical coverage of recording has varied over time. Therefore, we have developed a rigorous methodology to calculate changes, which is explained in Chapter 2.

The success of the first five years of BNM recording was crowned with the publication of *The Millennium Atlas of Butterflies in Britain and Ireland*.

The Butterfly Monitoring Scheme

Detailed population monitoring of butterflies commenced at a national scale in the UK in 1976 with the launch of the Butterfly Monitoring Scheme, co-ordinated by the Centre for Ecology and Hydrology and Joint Nature Conservation Committee. Under the scheme, observers make counts of butterfly numbers at specific sites by weekly recording along a fixed route (transect) under favourable weather conditions throughout the main butterfly flight period[5].

Compared with distribution recording under the BNM project, for which volunteers can do as much or as little as they wish, transect monitoring requires a significant commitment: ideally 26 transect walks per year, each of which might take 1–2 hours to complete, over many years. For this reason (and because of the limited capacity to co-ordinate the scheme centrally) the number of BMS sites is constrained. Initially, the scheme involved 34 sites across the UK, but this increased steadily to 134 sites in 2004. Most of the BMS transects are carried out at protected sites, such as nature reserves, with semi-natural habitats (biotopes).

All of this effort has proved extremely valuable. It provides a standardised annual measure of the changing status of butterfly species, which can be used to generate short-term trends; something that cannot be derived from distribution recording. Furthermore, BMS data have played a key role in many of the advances in knowledge of butterfly ecology in the UK over the past three decades[5]. Through the data, scientists have unravelled the dependence of butterfly populations on the climate[6]. Not only has this paved the way for assessments of the impact of global warming on our biodiversity, but it has also greatly helped our understanding of how landscape, land-use and habitat changes affect butterflies. The analysis of BMS data can allow for the over-riding effect of the weather, thus enabling other influences on particular butterfly populations to be detected. For example, site managers can assess the impact of small-scale habitat management and policy makers can monitor the effectiveness of national-scale agri-environment schemes[7].

4 Heath *et al*. 1984
5 Pollard and Yates 1993
6 e.g. Pollard 1988, Pollard and Yates 1993, Roy *et al*. 2001
7 Brereton *et al*. 2006

With an output of over a hundred scientific research papers and recent improvements in analysis of the data, the BMS has gone from strength to strength. Nevertheless, there is room for improvement in two main areas. Firstly, because of the limited number of sites in the scheme, there are insufficient data to generate population trends for some of the rarer species. Secondly, most BMS sites are protected areas that are managed, at least in part, with biodiversity conservation objectives. As a consequence, the national population trends generated by the scheme may not be representative of the landscape as a whole. Both of these limitations are now being addressed and the future of butterfly monitoring is brighter than ever (see overleaf).

Butterfly Conservation's Transect project

Although the number of sites contributing to the BMS has remained limited, the scheme's transect methodology developed by Dr Ernie Pollard has been taken up by many conservation organisations, landowners and amateur naturalists. The number of transects operating outside the BMS grew steadily at first, but increased rapidly after 1990. By 2003, over 500 transects were being recorded by more than 1,000 recorders, with 80 new ones established in that year alone[8]. Although some local co-ordination of results was already being undertaken by pioneering Branches of Butterfly Conservation, national collation and analysis of all these

8 Brereton *et al.* 2006

Butterfly transect monitoring has proved to be a popular, enjoyable and extremely useful activity, generating data with many important applications for habitat management, ecological research and policy development.

independent transects only commenced in 1998. Since then, support from the Department for Environment, Food and Rural Affairs (Defra) and its predecessor, the Ministry of Agriculture, Fisheries and Food (MAFF) has enabled Butterfly Conservation to co-ordinate independent transects (and other standardised survey data e.g. timed counts). This has not only allowed the collation and analysis of an important new data set, but has encouraged and trained the people who walk transects (most of whom are volunteers). It has also streamlined the flow of data, instigated new transects in under-recorded regions and led to the development of new analysis techniques and software.

Although most transects co-ordinated by Butterfly Conservation were started relatively recently and do not have the benefit of long time-series of data, the large number of monitored sites has enabled the calculation, for the first time, of reliable population trends for many of the rare and threatened species, which are of greatest concern to conservationists. Most of these are published in this book for the first time. In addition, although like BMS transects, much of the independent monitoring is carried out on protected sites, there is a much greater range and representation of different habitat and land-use types in the Butterfly Conservation data set. Indeed, the initial impetus to collate the data was to enable an assessment of the impact on butterfly populations of agri-environment schemes in the farmed landscape.

The future of recording and monitoring

To utilise fully the large effort devoted to recording transects throughout the UK, the Butterfly Conservation Transect project and the BMS have been merged into a single scheme. With funding from a multi-agency consortium led by Defra, the UK Butterfly Monitoring Scheme (UKBMS) commenced in spring 2006. The population data used in this book are based on this full set of transects. Over the coming years, work will continue to enhance butterfly monitoring in the UK and to develop butterfly biodiversity indicators. Development of a suitable method for monitoring populations of common butterflies in the wider landscape (akin to the Breeding Birds Survey run by the British Trust for Ornithology) is also underway and, further afield, efforts are being made to integrate transect data from other countries to produce European butterfly trends and an international biodiversity indicator.

At the same time, the BNM project has commenced its third five-year distribution survey (2005–09) and continues to collate new and historical records. Together, these distribution recording and population monitoring schemes will ensure the most complete and up-to-date foundation for the conservation of butterflies, their habitats, and other biodiversity.

We still need your help!

Almost all of the information presented in this book is based on data gathered by volunteers. You can contribute to future assessments of the state of butterflies by helping with recording and monitoring. Anyone can help. You could walk a transect regularly, survey under-recorded areas (not all of these are in remote parts of Britain and Ireland!) or simply note down sightings from your garden and surroundings. Please contact Butterfly Conservation 0870 7744309 or www.butterfly-conservation.org for more information.

Chapter 2 **Data and analysis**

The distribution maps and population trends for *The State of Butterflies in Britain and Ireland* are the product of two separate data sources and sets of analysis: one based on the recorded **distributions** of butterflies across the whole area (i.e. an estimate of species range or area of occupancy) and the other based on detailed **population monitoring** at selected sites (i.e. an estimate of abundance or population size).

Butterfly distributions

Distribution data

The distribution records used in this book were derived from the Butterflies for the New Millennium (BNM) data set (see p.1). The nature of BNM records was described at some length in *The Millennium Atlas*[1] and, since it has not changed substantially, only a few brief summary comments are included here.

BNM records comprise sightings of identified butterfly species at a location that has been described using a grid reference from a standard system (and often a place name as well) and within a certain time period. Most records since 1995 have an exact date (i.e. day), but some specify only a month or year. Recent records also typically include a measure of the number of individual butterflies seen but, since this is not related to search effort or weather conditions, it should not be used as a surrogate for population size (or even relative population size). Nevertheless, it can provide a useful guide to the breeding status of species (particularly for those with a colonial population structure) at individual sites.

Although the maps in this publication display species records at a spatial resolution of 10km x 10km grid squares (hereafter called 10km squares), 93% of all BNM records and 96% of 1995–2004 records have a resolution of either a 1km or 100m grid square. This precision is important for locating and conserving butterfly populations. The 10km square scale is used because it is the most appropriate for displaying species' distributions across the whole of Britain and Ireland.

The presence of immature stages is recorded in the BNM data set. This provides direct evidence of breeding and improves detectability by extending the time period for surveying and enabling recording in poor weather. Recorders specifically target the immature stages of certain species (e.g. Brown Hairstreak eggs or Marsh Fritillary larvae), but those of many others are also recorded, supplementing standard sightings of adult butterflies (e.g. Orange-tip, Purple Hairstreak and Northern Brown Argus eggs, and Large White, Small Tortoiseshell and Peacock larvae).

The BNM records meet a set of basic standards and are verified to identify and correct errors. However, recording is not normally directed and records are often opportunistic. Participants are encouraged to record any butterflies that they see, at any time of the year and in any location. However, some recorders undertake systematic searches of particular areas, target historically known colonies, or travel to under-recorded areas to help improve overall survey coverage.

With the completion of the latest phase of the BNM survey, there are now three time periods in which British and Irish butterflies have been surveyed comprehensively (i.e. >90% coverage at the 10km square scale): 1970–82, 1995–99 and 2000–04. Summary statistics and coverage maps are shown overleaf. These periods have been used in this book to prepare new distribution maps for all butterfly species that regularly breed in our islands.

1 Asher *et al.* 2001

Summary statistics of the BNM data set for the survey periods: 2000–04, 1995–99 and 1970–82.

		Overall	Britain and Isle of Man	Ireland	Channel Islands
2000–04	Total number of records	1,616,620	1,537,958	56,136	22,526
	% Coverage of 10km squares	96.4%	96.3%	96.5%	100%
1995–99	Total number of records	1,710,586	1,642,432	50,501	17,653
	% Coverage of 10km squares	98.0%	98.3%	96.9%	100%
1995–2004 combined	Total number of records	3,327,206	3,180,390	106,637	40,179
	% Coverage of 10km squares	99.3%	99.4%	99.1%	100%
1970–82	Total number of records	185,649	171,363	14,178	108
	% Coverage of 10km squares	90.3%	92.6%	84.6%	44%

Note: For the purposes of calculating % coverage, the total number of 10km squares for each major region is based on those required to cover the region, but does not include those marginal squares that enclose only small fragments of land.

The 1970–82 data set, compiled originally by the Biological Records Centre (BRC)[2], has been supplemented with additional historical data for the same period, contributed by local biological record centres and BNM local recording co-ordinators. The table of summary statistics (above) includes these extra data, which have added about 50,000 records in total.

The focus of *The State of Butterflies in Britain and Ireland* is on recent changes in the status of species, rather than on presenting a full historical account. Thus, pre-1970 historical records, which have already been published[3], have not been included on the maps or in the analysis. More records from the 1983–94 period have also been added to the BNM data set in recent years (bringing the total to over 790,000), but the geographical coverage is still patchy and not suitable for direct comparison with the more comprehensive earlier (i.e. 1970–82) and later (i.e. 1995–2004) surveys.

In total, at the time of writing, nearly 4.5 million butterfly records are held on the BNM database, spanning the period 1690–2005.

Choice of date periods for comparison

A high level of BNM recording was achieved in the 2000–04 period. Over 1.6 million butterfly records were added to the data set, covering 98% of the number of 10km squares recorded in 1995–99. This is a considerable achievement as the history of biological recording suggests that survey effort typically declines sharply after the publication of a high-profile atlas. The success is a tribute to the sustained enthusiasm of voluntary recorders spurred on, not only by the BNM project, but also by a number of local atlas initiatives and an increasing appreciation of the rapid pace of change affecting our butterfly fauna. The continued recording not only tracks ongoing distribution changes through time, but also adds to the 1995–99 survey to provide a more comprehensive modern data set to contrast with the historical baseline, thus improving the accuracy of status change assessments.

On average, 333,000 records from 2,885 squares were received per year during the 1995–2004 recording period. The major outbreak of foot-and-mouth disease in 2001 caused a dip in recording levels as access was restricted to much of the countryside in Britain and Ireland.

2000–04

- 'New' squares
- 'Lost' squares
- Recorded in both periods

Map showing the distribution of squares visited in 2000–04, but not in 1995–99 ('New' squares: 50 squares in total), those visited in 1995–99, but not in 2000–04 ('Lost' squares: 113) and those visited in both recent survey periods. Almost all squares (96%) were surveyed in both periods.

2 Heath *et al*. 1984

3 Asher *et al*. 2001, Heath *et al*. 1984

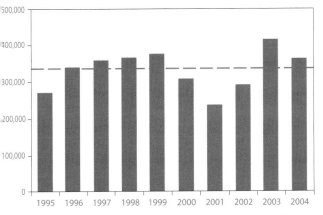

The number of records received each year in the BNM database (1995–2004). The dashed line indicates the 10-year average (333,000 records).

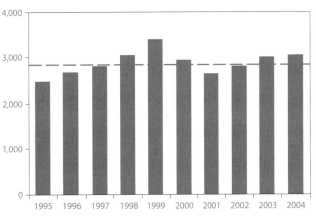

The number of 10km squares recorded in each year (1995–2004). The dashed line indicates the 10-year average (2,885 squares).

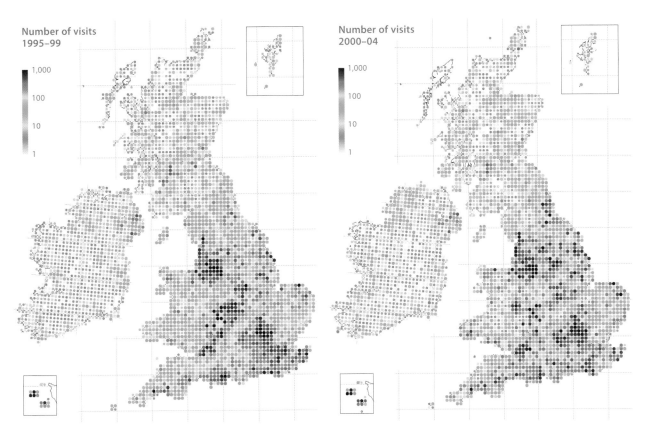

Number of visits 1995–99

Number of visits 2000–04

Comparison of visit density (on a log scale) in the two recent five-year survey periods. 'Visits' equate to unique combinations of recorder, grid reference and date in each 10km square.

Although the total number of records for the 2000–04 period is comparable with that for the 1995–99 period, and the overall distribution of records is similar, there are some regional differences, as illustrated by the maps of recording effort above. For example, there was a higher level of recording in Yorkshire, north-east England, Somerset and County Donegal in 2000–04, but a lower level in the West Midlands region of England, Ayrshire and the Western Isles.

The combination of the 1995–99 and 2000–04 data provides a 10-year data set that achieves over 97% coverage of 10km squares across all country areas (see table overleaf). This achievement is particularly notable for Scotland, where areas with low human population density pose a significant challenge for recording.

Country statistics of the BNM data set for the survey periods: 2000–04, 1995–99 and 1970–82.		England	Scotland	Wales
2000–04	Total number of records	1,406,782	63,487	88,228
	% Coverage of 10km squares	99.2%	90.5%	98.2%
1995–99	Total number of records	1,591,347	70,501	90,329
	% Coverage of 10km squares	99.9%	94.6%	99.6%
1995–2004 combined	Total number of records	2,908,129	133,988	178,557
	% Coverage of 10km squares	100%	97.0%	99.6%
1970–82	Total number of records	138,719	16,090	19,573
	% Coverage of 10km squares	98.1%	82.8%	97.9%

Because of the high overall level of coverage achieved in the period 1995–2004, a comparison of data from this period with those from 1970–82 was used to provide the best basis for quantifying historical distribution change in this book.

Analysis of distribution change

The BNM data set provides an excellent source of location information for butterflies. Without such information, much assessment and action for the conservation of butterflies would be impossible. Distribution data, interpreted with care, also provide information on species' trends through time. For example, recent research using the BNM data set has indicated that even static distribution patterns (i.e. from a single snapshot survey) contain reliable signals of species'

Maps showing the number of 'visits' in each time period, displayed on a logarithmic scale. Note that there is a factor of 10 difference in scale between the two maps, reflecting the large difference in overall recording effort between the periods.

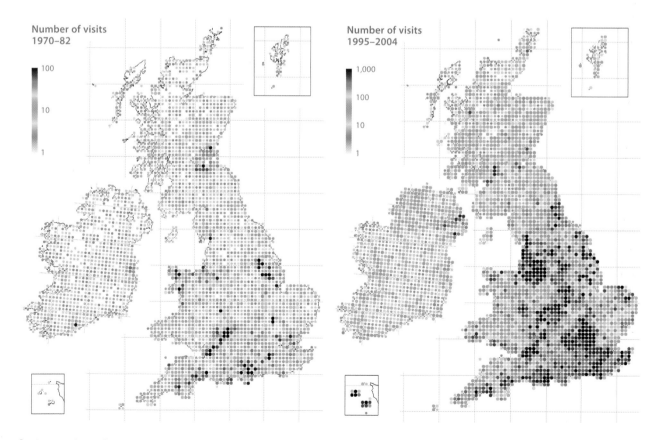

past and future status[4]. Declining species show sparse, fragmented distributions relative to their distribution size, reflecting the extinction process; expanding species show denser, more aggregated distributions, reflecting colonisation.

When distribution data exist from two or more time periods, as is the case with the BNM project, then comparison can yield temporal trends for species. However, care is needed in such comparisons to ensure that results are not distorted by inherent biases in this type of data[5]. Recording effort is the most important factor that needs to be taken into account when using the BNM data to assess changes in butterfly status in Britain and Ireland.

As shown in the previous section, recording effort (e.g. total number of records) in the 1995–99 and 2000–04 periods was much greater than in the 1970–82 baseline. Furthermore, this overall increase in recording effort is complicated by considerable regional and local variation. The differences in recording density and coverage between the periods 1970–82 and 1995–2004 are clear in the maps (opposite) showing the number of 'visits' (defined as records with a unique combination of recorder, grid reference and date) per 10km square across Britain and Ireland on a logarithmic scale (note that the logarithmic scale is different on each map).

The distribution analysis presented in *The Millennium Atlas*[6] was relatively crude and, other than it being noted as a significant factor, little account was taken of recording effort variation between the two survey periods being compared.

The large difference in recording effort, both in the overall level and in the pattern of coverage, between two time periods, can result in misleading trends if these are based on a simple comparison of the number of occupied squares for each species in each period. Increased recording in the more recent period is likely to have resulted in an apparent increase in the distribution of most species, as previously unknown colonies are discovered, even when their ranges may actually be stable or decreasing.

Sub-sampling

A new, more sophisticated, analytical technique (termed sub-sampling) has been applied successfully to the BNM data from *The Millennium Atlas*[7]. The results correlated closely with trends from butterfly population monitoring, suggesting that distribution change (even at the relatively coarse 10km square resolution) can be a valid surrogate for population change[8].

The distribution trends presented in this book were calculated using a further refinement of the sub-sampling analysis. The technique provides a way to reduce the bias resulting from differences in recording intensity in the two periods 1970–82 and 1995–2004 by producing an approximate equalisation of recording effort (see box). We believe this approach provides a good assessment of distribution change between recording periods.

Only those 10km squares that were visited in both periods were included in the analysis.

Sub-sampling method

For each period, the total number of visits to sites in each 10km square surveyed in both periods was counted, as follows:

The total numbers of fully-dated record cards (D cards), month-only cards (M cards) and year-only cards (Y cards) were summed, along with the total number of species records under each category, at both 10km and 100km square resolution. M and Y cards with less than a threshold number of species, equal to the average for fully-dated cards, were counted as D cards.

For each 100km square, the average number of species per card for D cards (N_D), M cards (N_M) and Y cards (N_Y), respectively, were calculated.

For each 10km square, an effective number of visits was calculated, using the formula:

$$V_{eff} = (\text{No. of D cards}) + (\text{No. of M cards} \times N_M/N_D) + (\text{No. of Y cards} \times N_Y/N_D)$$

The ratio, R, between the effective number of visits in each 10km square in the recent period and the effective number of visits in the historic period, was calculated. Where the ratio was greater than 1, record cards were sub-sampled at a frequency of 1/R. So, for example, if R=8 for a particular 10km square (i.e. the square had received 8 times as many visits in the recent period), then a random-number algorithm was used to select an average of only 1 out of 8 cards (on a random basis) from the **recent** data for that 10km square; others were rejected.

Where the ratio, R, was less than 1, then only a fraction R of the **historic** visit records were accepted for that 10km square. For example, if R=0.7, then a randomly selected 7 out of 10 records were accepted and 3 out of 10 were rejected.

---

4 Wilson *et al*. 2004
5 Dennis *et al*. 1999, 2006a, Dennis and Thomas 2000, Thomas and Abery 1995
6 Asher *et al*. 2001
7 J.A. Thomas *et al*. 2004, Warren *et al*. 2001a
8 Thomas 2005, Warren *et al*. 2001a

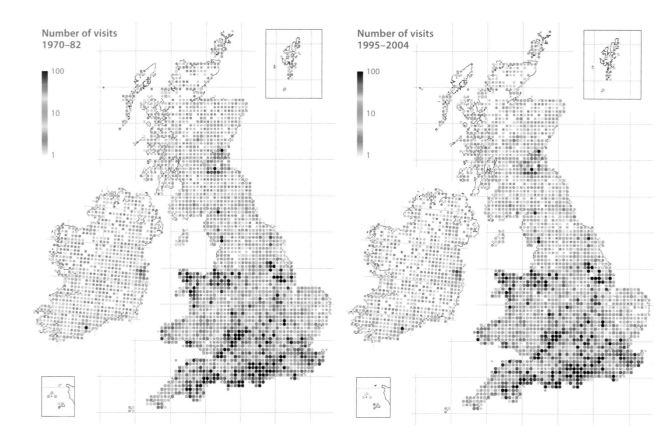

Maps showing the number of effective visits on a logarithmic scale allocated by sub-sampling to each 10km square in the two main time periods being analysed.

Over 96% of the 10km squares for 1995–2004 were subject to sub-sampling: about 4% of squares required ratios of over 100; five squares required ratios of over 1,000, with the maximum being 3,300. For the 1970–82 data set, less than 4% of 10km squares required sub-sampling, at ratios up to a maximum of nine.

The effect of the sub-sampling on the distribution of recording effort is illustrated above with typical sub-sampled maps showing the number of 'effective visits' (calculated as described in the box on p.9) for each time period. Note that the logarithmic scale, representing number of visits, is the same for both maps.

The sub-sampled maps above show a much more similar distribution of recording effort between the two time periods than the unmodified maps (see p.8). Within the limits of small differences due to the random sampling, the coverage of effective visits to each square is virtually identical, and allows a more reliable estimate of distribution change to be calculated.

Calculation of species' distribution trends

To reduce the effect of random fluctuations, the sub-sampling was repeated 30 times, using the same set of effective visit ratios, to generate a set of 30 pairs of distribution maps for each species (each pair comprising one map for each date period).

For each species, the number of 10km squares where the butterfly was recorded in one, other or both survey periods was counted for each of the 30 pairs of maps.

The difference between the number of square gains (where a species appears in a square in the recent period where it was not recorded in the historic period) and the number of square losses (where a species does not appear in a square in the recent period, where it had been recorded in the historic period), divided by the total number of squares for that species in the historic period, provided the distribution trend for the species for each pair of sub-sampled maps.

The trend is slightly different for each pair of maps because of variations arising from the random rejection of record cards. The final species' distribution trends presented in this book were calculated as the mean of the trends from the 30 rounds of sub-sampling. A standard deviation from the mean was calculated for each final trend to provide an estimate of statistical uncertainty.

Distribution trends were calculated across the whole geographic area of Britain and Ireland, across Britain and the Isle of Man only, and across England, Scotland, Wales and Ireland separately. For this purpose, records from 10km squares overlapping the borders between England and Scotland and between England and Wales were included in the analysis for each country, so there is a small degree of overlap (1–2% of squares) between adjacent countries.

It important to note that, although the sub-sampling method described here goes a long way to reducing bias due to changing patterns of recording effort, it does not eliminate it. For example, sub-sampling takes no account of the time of year at which visits occurred. If most of the visits to a 10km square in one recording period were in midsummer, then spring and late summer species will be disproportionately under-represented, and midsummer species over-represented; the analysis will not eliminate this type of bias, and it will not be accounted for in the statistical uncertainties quoted. Nonetheless, sub-sampling provides a much better way to estimate trends between recording periods than a simple comparison of the number of occupied squares.

Butterfly populations

Population data
The butterfly population data used in this book come from the UK Butterfly Monitoring Scheme (UKBMS) recently formed from the merger of the long-running Butterfly Monitoring Scheme with Butterfly Conservation's co-ordination of 'independent' transects (see Chapter 1 for details). For the majority of species assessed, only data from butterfly transects have been used, but there are other methods of recording butterfly population data, such as timed counts. Timed count data are collated by the UKBMS and have been used to supplement transect data in the assessment of High Brown Fritillary and Heath Fritillary population levels for this publication.

Trends have been calculated only for Britain. Currently, there are insufficient transects in Ireland to enable the assessment of butterfly population trends there. A number of transects have been established in Ireland in recent years, and a monitoring scheme has been initiated in Jersey, so it should be possible to present further trends in the future.

Population data are time-consuming to collect but can yield very useful information not only on how butterflies are faring, but also on how factors such as habitat management and climate affect populations.

Transect monitoring
The methodology and development of transect monitoring for butterflies has been reviewed in detail elsewhere[9]. In brief, a fixed-route walk (transect) is established at a site and butterflies are recorded along the route on a regular (weekly) basis under reasonable weather conditions for a number of years. Transect routes are chosen to sample evenly the habitat types and management activity on sites. Care is taken in choosing a transect route as it must then remain fixed to enable butterfly sightings to be compared from year to year. Transects are typically about 2–4km long, taking between 45 minutes and two hours to walk, and are divided into sections corresponding to different habitat or management units.

Butterflies are recorded in a fixed width band (typically 5m wide) along the transect each week from the beginning of April until the end of September yielding, ideally, 26 counts per year. Transect walks are undertaken between 10.45am and 3.45pm and only when weather conditions are suitable for butterfly

9 e.g. Pollard and Yates 1993

activity: dry conditions, wind speed less than Beaufort scale 5, and temperature 13°C or greater if there is at least 60% sunshine, or more than 17°C if overcast. Due to the vagaries of the British and Irish weather, it is rare in practice to achieve a full set of 26 weekly counts. However, a small number of missing values can be estimated using other counts during the season[10].

Single species (as opposed to normal 'all species') transects have been increasingly established in recent years. Whilst such transects must follow the standard methodology and must record populations at least once a week throughout the flight period, the focus on a single (or small number of) species reduces both the time required to walk each transect and, more significantly, the number of weekly counts. With many demands on the time of site management staff and volunteer recorders, this reduced method has enabled population monitoring of particular threatened butterflies to be undertaken when otherwise it would not have been possible.

By regularly recording a fixed route in standardised conditions, the number of butterflies seen on a transect can be compared from year to year.

Transect coverage

The butterfly transect method has proved popular with site managers and volunteer recorders, and has provided a wealth of high quality scientific output. The number of transects has risen consistently since the start of the scheme in 1976, and this growth has increased in recent years (particularly in England and Scotland) as a result of Butterfly Conservation's promotion of monitoring. The UKBMS has collated data from over 1,000 transects so far, representing nearly 150,000 weekly walks and records of over 10.5 million individual butterflies! Even so, there are other transects that are not yet part of the UKBMS.

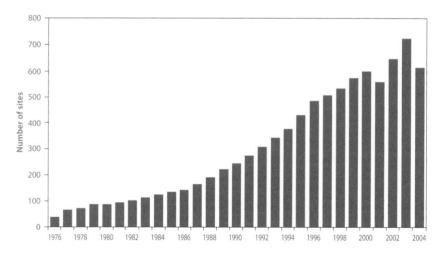

Number of transect sites per year in the UKBMS data set. The reduced number of transects with data in 2001 results from access restrictions to monitored sites because of foot-and-mouth disease.

Number of UKBMS transects per decade for each country.

Period	England	Wales	Scotland	Northern Ireland	Total
1976–79	63	11	11	1	86
1980–89	202	12	14	1	229
1990–99	606	15	23	3	647
2000–04	805	20	55	4	884
Total	917	29	62	4	1,012

10 Rothery and Roy 2001

The intensive recording effort required for population monitoring means, inevitably, that only a sample of important butterfly sites can be covered. Despite the success of the method and the UKBMS, it is vital that an assessment is made of whether these existing transects adequately represent the overall national populations of butterfly species. This enables an informed judgement to be made as to whether population trends derived from the UKBMS are representative of the landscape as a whole.

Such assessments of the coverage of monitoring transects have been carried out recently by species, Government region, country and habitat type[11]. The overall conclusion is that population data are considered sufficient to represent the trends of butterflies in semi-natural habitats, but not in the landscape as a whole. Coverage in England is much better than in the other UK countries at present. Here, most species of conservation concern (including UK BAP Priority Species), which are restricted to semi-natural habitats, are adequately covered in many areas. However, more work is needed to improve the representativeness of monitoring in Northern Ireland, Scotland and Wales. Development plans have been instigated to achieve this, and to strengthen further the transect network across England.

Population trends of wider countryside species may not reflect the fortunes of these butterflies in Britain as a whole (i.e. away from special sites). As the management of semi-natural areas is expected to be more favourable for butterflies than that of the wider countryside, it has been suggested that population trends from transect data may present an overly optimistic assessment of both decreases and increases.

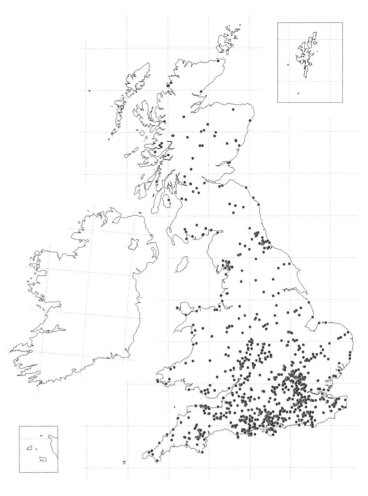

The location of butterfly monitoring transects and timed counts in Britain used in the analysis of species' population trends. The UKBMS contains data from additional sites in Britain and from Northern Ireland, but these have not been utilised in the analysis presented in this book.

Timed counts

Timed counts represent an alternative and rapid method of assessing the abundance of individual habitat specialist butterfly species at a site[12]. They are particularly appropriate for species that (1) occur in remote areas where intensive monitoring is impractical and (2) have populations that shift within sites comprised of large areas of semi-natural habitat (e.g. large forests, moorland). Normally only one or two timed counts are undertaken at a site each year and they typically focus on a single target species. In a timed count, a zigzag walk is made across the whole flight area, ensuring even coverage, and the number of butterflies is counted per minute of search effort. A measure of population size is then calculated by scaling the count to peak abundance, with reference to local transect data.

If carried out year on year, timed counts can contribute to the calculation of population trends for species (as for the High Brown Fritillary and Heath Fritillary in this publication). However, timed counts cannot be used in isolation, as local transect data are required for calibration. Thus, whilst transects remain essential, timed counts can help to increase greatly the number of monitored sites in areas where there are few butterfly recorders.

For example, whilst a high proportion of High Brown Fritillary colonies in north-west England are monitored by transects, there are few transects in other areas such as south-west England and Wales. A British population trend for the species based solely on transect data would be biased heavily by the fortunes of colonies in the north-west. By including timed count data from other regions, a more representative estimate of the overall trend can be generated.

11 Brereton *et al*. 2003, Wigglesworth *et al*. 2005
12 Warren *et al*. 1984

Collated indices of abundance

Both transect counts and timed counts are used primarily to produce an annual estimate (site index) of the abundance of a butterfly species at a site. These site indices have been shown to relate closely to other, more intensive, measures of population size such as mark/release/recapture methods[13]. The site index can be thought of as a relative measure of the overall population size, being a more or less constant proportion of the number of butterflies actually present. The proportion of a butterfly population seen by any recorder on a particular visit is likely to vary according to species and sex; some butterflies, such as the Marbled White, are much more conspicuous than others, such as the Dingy Skipper, and males are often more conspicuous than females[14]. Furthermore, the transect method may not be equally appropriate for all species. For example, tree-canopy species such as the Purple Hairstreak, White-letter Hairstreak or Purple Emperor are difficult to record, and monitoring trends for these species should be treated with caution until further research has been undertaken to validate the method.

Although they are relative measures, site indices can be combined to derive regional and national collated indices and be used to estimate trends over time. However, this collation is not a straightforward calculation because not all of the 1,000+ transect sites in the UKBMS data set have been recorded each year. Some transect sites have operated for over 20 years, but the majority have not and some have only been recorded for a few years. A statistical model is needed to produce a regional or national index of how butterfly populations have changed each year.

A number of techniques have been used to calculate national and regional collated indices of abundance from wildlife monitoring data[15]. In common with most butterfly and bird monitoring schemes in Europe, a log-linear Poisson regression model, as performed by the statistical software TRIM[16], has been used to analyse the UKBMS data for this publication. In this approach, the expected count at a particular site in a given year is assumed to be a product of a site and a year effect. Put simply, the model attempts to take account of the fact that, for a particular butterfly species, some years are better than others (the year effect), typically due to the weather, and some sites support larger populations than others (the site effect), for example because of different habitat conditions. In this way, for years where a transect site has not been recorded, the model estimates a site index that allows for the general conditions of the year in question and how favourable the site is. The national collated index is then calculated as the mean (on a log scale) of the estimated and recorded site indices for each year.

Collated indices have been calculated for butterflies (49 species in total) that have been recorded from a minimum of five sites per year, although many have been monitored at a much larger number of sites. For most species, this provided collated index values from 1976 to 2004, showing how the overall abundance of each species has changed over this time period. The regression slope of log collated index on years was used to measure the trends over time both for the full time period and for the last 10 years (1995–2004). The significance of these long-term and 10-year trends was determined by the correlation coefficient between the log collated index and years[17].

Summary

We are fortunate to have two excellent sources of volunteer-gathered data from which to assess the changing status of butterflies. Although each data set has its strengths and weaknesses, they complement each other to provide a highly effective national monitoring system for butterflies, which could be replicated in many other nations around the world (as has been demonstrated already in some European countries)[18].

13 Pollard *et al.* 1986
14 Dennis and Sparks 2006, Dennis *et al.* 2006a
15 ter Braak *et al.* 1994
16 Pannekoek and van Strien 1996
17 Pollard *et al.* 1995
18 Thomas 2005

Chapter 3 **Species accounts**

Guide to content and layout

Names
The vernacular names and taxonomic order of species follow Emmet and Heath (1990). Scientific names of butterflies follow the Fauna Europaea Web Service (2004) Fauna Europaea version 1.1 (http://www.faunaeur.org), accessed on 18 October 2005. Where generic names have been revised recently, the previous genus is included in brackets. Vernacular and scientific names of plants follow Stace (1997).

Status and trends
The status of each species within the UK Biodiversity Action Plan (BAP) is given. This is based on the original classification of species for the Plan[1], modified to reflect proposed changes in the 2006 review of the UK BAP[2]. The outcome of this review will not be made public until the end of 2006 (at the earliest); thus, we have listed the new proposed species as 'candidates'. National priorities have been developed for some countries within the UK, but this process is incomplete and details are not included here. The Republic of Ireland's National Biodiversity Plan[3] does not yet include any species action plans for butterflies, but the process of developing plans is ongoing.

Distribution trends for Britain (including the Isle of Man) are based on a comparison of the Butterflies for the New Millennium (BNM) data for 1995–2004 with those for the 1970–82 period. The trends have been derived by an approach (termed sub-sampling) that seeks to reduce bias due to variable levels of recording effect in different date periods and geographical regions (see Chapter 2 for details).

A similar analysis was carried out for Ireland. However, it is the opinion of the authors, the Dublin Naturalists' Field Club and the Northern Ireland Branch of Butterfly Conservation that distribution data for the whole of Ireland are insufficient to enable an identical presentation of changes there since the 1970s. Taking into account the analysis results, together with the considered views of Irish recorders, we have decided instead to use broad categories to indicate distribution change: *Severe decrease* (50% or greater reduction in the number of occupied 10km squares); *medium decrease* (30–49%); *small decrease* (10–29%); *stable* (less than 10% reduction or increase); *increase* (10% or greater increase in the number of occupied 10km squares); and *insufficient data*. Some parts of Ireland have been thoroughly recorded and apparent increases in species distributions on the maps in this book probably reflect increased recording effort. It is hoped that continuing survey effort will enable a more accurate assessment of change in the future.

Population trends for Britain are based on transect monitoring data from the UK Butterfly Monitoring Scheme (UKBMS) database (except for those of the High Brown Fritillary and Heath Fritillary, which also include timed count data). Trends that are statistically significant (i.e. P<0.05) are indicated by an asterisk within the arrow symbol. A minimum of five monitored sites per year is required to generate

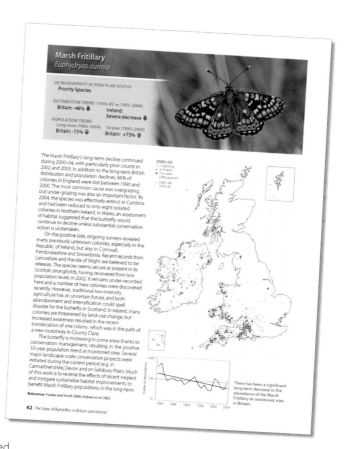

Marsh Fritillary
Euphydryas aurinia

UK BIODIVERSITY ACTION PLAN STATUS
Priority Species

DISTRIBUTION TREND (1970–82 vs 1995–2004)
Britain: -46% ⬇   Ireland: Severe decrease ⬇

POPULATION TREND
Long-term (1983–2004)   10-year (1995–2004)
Britain: -73% ⬇   Britain: +73% ⬆

The Marsh Fritillary's long-term decline continued during 2000–04, with particularly poor counts in 2002 and 2003. In addition to the long-term British distribution and population declines, 66% of colonies in England were lost between 1990 and 2000. The most common cause was overgrazing, but under-grazing was also an important factor. By 2004, the species was effectively extinct in Cumbria and had been reduced to only eight isolated colonies in Northern Ireland. In Wales, an assessment of habitat suggested that the butterfly would continue to decline unless substantial conservation action is undertaken.

On the positive side, ongoing surveys revealed many previously unknown colonies, especially in the Republic of Ireland, but also in Cornwall, Pembrokeshire and Snowdonia. Recent records from Lancashire and the Isle of Wight are believed to be releases. The species seems secure at present in its Scottish strongholds, having recovered from low population levels in 2002. It remains under-recorded here and a number of new colonies were discovered recently. However, traditional low-intensity agriculture has an uncertain future, and both abandonment and intensification could spell disaster for the butterfly in Scotland. In Ireland, many colonies are threatened by land-use change, but increased awareness resulted in the recent translocation of one colony, which was in the path of a new motorway in County Clare.

The butterfly is increasing in some areas thanks to conservation management, resulting in the positive 10-year population trend at monitored sites. Several major landscape-scale conservation projects were initiated during the current period (e.g. in Carmarthenshire, Devon and on Salisbury Plain). Much of this work is to reverse the effects of recent neglect and instigate sustainable habitat improvements to benefit Marsh Fritillary populations in the long-term.

There has been a significant long-term decrease in the abundance of the Marsh Fritillary at monitored sites in Britain.

References: Fowles and Smith 2006, Hobson et al. 2002

62 *The State of Butterflies in Britain and Ireland*

1   UK Biodiversity Group 1998
2   Bourn *et al.* 2005
3   Department of Arts, Heritage, Gaeltacht and the Islands 2002

a population trend for a species. A few species do not meet this criterion or are insufficiently sampled and, therefore, have no population trend (Swallowtail, Brown Hairstreak, Black Hairstreak, Glanville Fritillary and Mountain Ringlet). The starting point for the long-term trend is also affected by the need for a minimum of five sites in each year, so not all species have a population trend going back to 1976 (the start of the original Butterfly Monitoring Scheme). Finally, there are no population trends for Small Skipper and Essex Skipper, as these two species are not normally distinguished during transect monitoring in Britain. Chapter 2 provides details of the analysis method.

No population trends could be given for Ireland as there are too few monitoring transects to enable reliable trends to be calculated.

Distribution map

The distribution map for each species[4] shows the 10km square distribution as determined by the 2000–04 survey (coloured dots), together with data from two previous periods: 1995–99 (open circles indicating 10km squares where a species was recorded in 1995–99 but not in the recent survey) and 1970–82 (crosses indicating 10km squares where a species was recorded in 1970–82 but not in either of the other periods). For each square, records from the more recent survey period take precedence over those from earlier periods. Known or suspected introductions, reintroductions and releases are not distinguished from other records on the map, although some are mentioned in the text. Some records resulting from these activities are excluded from the BNM data by local co-ordinators during the verification process.

The coloured dots in the 2000–04 period indicate the maximum number of individuals seen on any single visit to a location within that 10km square. Records of immature stages are placed in the 2–9 seen category.

It should be noted that the distribution map does not show the same comparison of survey periods used to assess distribution trends for species. For the latter, the combined 1995–2004 data have been compared to the 1970–82 survey. However, we felt it important and interesting to map the 1995–99 and 2000–04 periods separately.

Population plot

The population plot shows, on a logarithmic scale, the collated index values derived from transect monitoring in Britain (from the UKBMS database). The collated index is a measure of the relative abundance or population level of each species at monitored sites. A minimum of five sites per year is required to calculate the index and for this reason not all plots start in 1976, when transect monitoring commenced at a national scale. The index is scaled relative to the average for the entire series, shown as a dotted line on the plot. Thus, if the index for a particular year is above the dotted line, the population level of the species was higher than the long-term average in that year (and vice versa). The long-term population trend is shown as a coloured line.

Species account text

The brief text that accompanies each species account aims to reflect changes in status during the 2000–04 period, in particular. Thus, it provides interpretation of this current period as shown on the distribution map and population plot. Information on European status, where mentioned, is derived from the *Red Data Book of European Butterflies*[5]. We have not attempted to repeat or update ecological information for each species, nor give an account of their historical distribution change. Readers are referred to *The Millennium Atlas of Butterflies in Britain and Ireland*[6] for such information.

References

Only references that are of immediate relevance to the text are listed. For a more complete list of references covering the ecology and conservation of butterflies, please consult *The Millennium Atlas*.

4 Except the maps for Réal's Wood White and Large Blue, which show different date periods
5 van Swaay and Warren 1999
6 Asher *et al.* 2001

Chequered Skipper
Carterocephalus palaemon

UK BIODIVERSITY ACTION PLAN STATUS
Priority Species

DISTRIBUTION TREND (1970–82 vs 1995–2004)
Britain: -38% ⬇

POPULATION TREND
Britain: insufficient data

There has been no substantial change in the status of the Chequered Skipper in the 2000–04 period. The species remains restricted to a small region of western Scotland, where it is still under-recorded and, therefore, the extent of its distribution is not fully established.

A few new colonies were discovered during the current survey, mainly at the northern edge of the butterfly's range, and recorders are urged to explore other suitable sites in this area.

Starting in the late 1990s, trials were conducted at Chambers Wood in Lincolnshire (dot shown on map), with a view to reintroducing Chequered Skippers there. However, the studies concluded that a reintroduction would be unsuccessful at the current time because there was insufficient habitat available within the wood and surrounding landscape.

The long-term distribution decline of this species is due to its extinction in England in 1976. The Chequered Skipper's status has not improved and it remains a UK BAP Priority Species. In addition, there are continuing concerns that exclusion of grazing from open woodlands in western Scotland may cause a deterioration of this rare species' habitat.

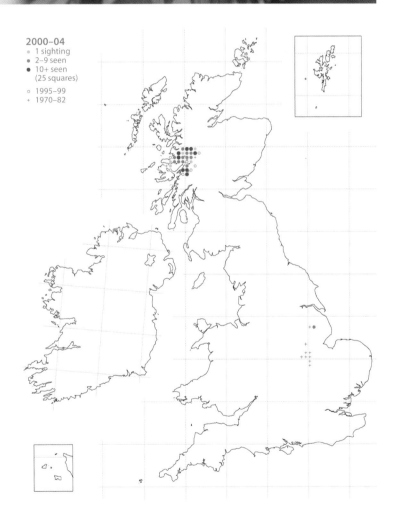

2000–04
- 1 sighting
- 2–9 seen
- 10+ seen (25 squares)
- 1995–99
+ 1970–82

Small Skipper
Thymelicus sylvestris

UK BIODIVERSITY ACTION PLAN STATUS
Not listed

DISTRIBUTION TREND (1970–82 vs 1995–2004)
Britain: +4% ⬆

POPULATION TREND
Britain: insufficient data

The Small Skipper continued to expand its range steadily northwards during the 2000–04 period (see map on p.78). New 10km square records in Northumberland have brought the distribution to within a few miles of the Scottish border in several places, and the Small Skipper will undoubtedly reach Scotland in the near future, possibly within the next five years.

The butterfly has also colonised new territory in north Yorkshire, northern Lancashire and Cumbria. New 10km squares have been recorded in north-west Wales, although here it is more difficult to separate genuine range expansion from past under-recording.

No population trend was calculated for this species, as Small and Essex Skippers are not normally counted separately on transects. However, distribution data suggest that the Small Skipper has done well in Britain since the 1970s and it is not considered a conservation priority.

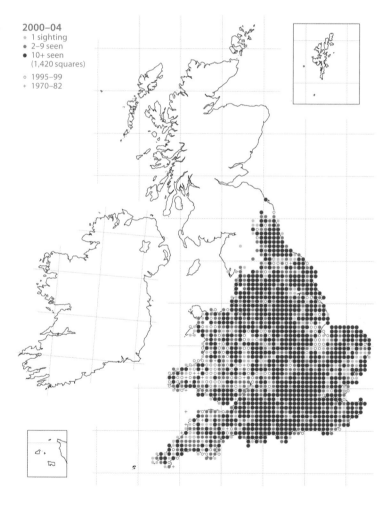

2000–04
- 1 sighting
- 2–9 seen
- 10+ seen
  (1,420 squares)
○ 1995–99
+ 1970–82

Essex Skipper
Thymelicus lineola

UK BIODIVERSITY ACTION PLAN STATUS
Not listed

DISTRIBUTION TREND (1970–82 vs 1995–2004)
Britain: +46% ⬆

POPULATION TREND
Britain: insufficient data

The Essex Skipper has shown the greatest percentage increase in distribution of any resident species since the 1970s and many additional areas were colonised along the expanding range margin during the 2000–04 period (see map on p.78). The biggest gains were in the north, particularly in Nottinghamshire, Derbyshire and southern Yorkshire. The butterfly also colonised southern Yorkshire by a different route: crossing the Humber to establish a population at Spurn Head.

In the west, the Essex Skipper reached Wales (Monmouthshire) in 2000 and has continued to spread westwards in the West Midlands' counties and through Dorset and Somerset.

Records for the current period in Devon and Cornwall are intriguing, as the species was resident historically in these counties. Further survey work and confirmation of identification is needed to ascertain the true distribution in the far south-west.

Although no population trend was calculated for this species (because Essex Skippers are not normally counted separately from Small Skippers during transect monitoring), the large increase in distribution indicates that the butterfly is doing well and is not of conservation concern.

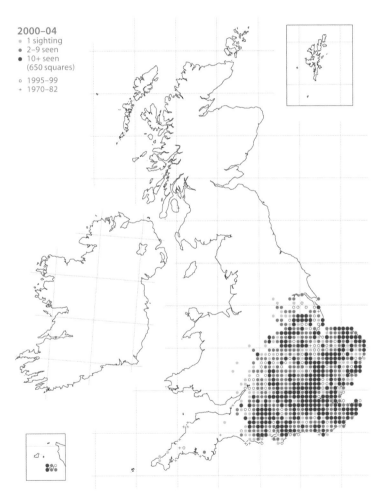

2000–04
- 1 sighting
- 2–9 seen
- 10+ seen
  (650 squares)
- 1995–99
- 1970–82

Lulworth Skipper
Thymelicus acteon

UK BIODIVERSITY ACTION PLAN STATUS
Candidate Priority Species

DISTRIBUTION TREND (1970–82 vs 1995–2004)
Britain: -15% ⬇

POPULATION TREND
Long-term (1992–2004)   10-year (1995–2004)
Britain: -13% ⬇   Britain: +79% ⬆

There has been no substantial change in the status of the Lulworth Skipper in the 2000–04 period. The species remains restricted to south Dorset, although it maintains very large populations at suitable sites within this limited range.

2000 was the best year in the 2000–04 period for the butterfly, with population levels in the other years being close to the long-term average. The positive 10-year population trend is due to the species recovering from particularly poor years in 1996 and 1997.

Although the distribution of this species has remained approximately stable in Britain since the 1970s, the Lulworth Skipper has been identified as a vulnerable species at the European scale due to its severe decline in many central and northern countries. As a result of the serious downward trend in continental Europe, the butterfly has been put forward as a candidate for Priority Species status in the 2006 UK BAP review.

Reference: Bourn and Thomas 2002

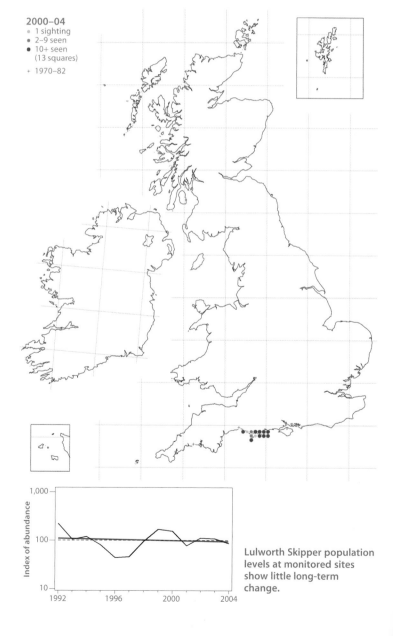

2000–04
- 1 sighting
- 2–9 seen
- 10+ seen (13 squares)
+ 1970–82

Lulworth Skipper population levels at monitored sites show little long-term change.

Silver-spotted Skipper
Hesperia comma

UK BIODIVERSITY ACTION PLAN STATUS
Priority Species – proposed for downgrading to Species of Conservation Concern

DISTRIBUTION TREND (1970–82 vs 1995–2004)
Britain: +4% ⬆

POPULATION TREND
Long-term (1979–2004)   10-year (1995–2004)
Britain: +1,524% ⬆   Britain: +2% ⬆

Although still a rare species, the fortunes of the Silver-spotted Skipper have been transformed since the 1970s. At monitored sites, abundance increased by an average of 12% per year between 1979 and 2004, and its distribution also increased substantially. The butterfly was recorded in only 21 10km squares in the 1970–82 period and a targeted survey in 1982 found just 68 populations in Britain. A repeat survey carried out in 2000 identified 257 populations: over a threefold increase. The BNM data mirror this great improvement: 43 10km squares were occupied in the 1995–2004 period, of which 12 were recorded only in the current (2000–04) phase of recording (see map on p.78).

At monitored sites, the rate of population increase seems to have levelled off in recent years. Nevertheless, population levels were well above the long-term average in all five years of the current period. Indeed, 2003 was the best year yet recorded for the butterfly at monitored sites.

The improvement is thought to be due to three factors that have improved the quantity and quality of chalk grassland habitat available to the Silver-spotted Skipper: conservation management to maintain a short, sparse turf and prevent scrub invasion; increasing rabbit populations (which also help maintain suitable turf); and climate change. Warmer temperatures have increased the extent of breeding habitat to include areas that were previously too cool for the butterfly (e.g. longer vegetation and west- and east-facing hillsides).

As a result of this change in status, the Silver-spotted Skipper has been proposed for downgrading in the UK BAP, from Priority Species to Species of Conservation Concern.

References: Davies *et al.* 2005, 2006, C.D. Thomas *et al.* 2001a

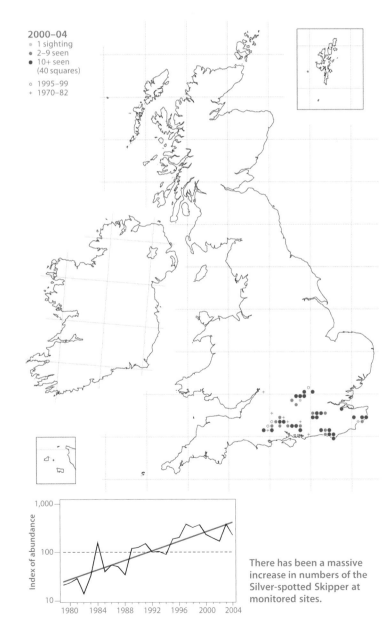

2000–04
- 1 sighting
- 2–9 seen
- 10+ seen
  (40 squares)
○ 1995–99
+ 1970–82

There has been a massive increase in numbers of the Silver-spotted Skipper at monitored sites.

Large Skipper
Ochlodes sylvanus

UK BIODIVERSITY ACTION PLAN STATUS
Not listed

DISTRIBUTION TREND (1970–82 vs 1995–2004)
Britain: -12% ⬇

POPULATION TREND
Long-term (1976–2004)   10-year (1995–2004)
Britain: +12% ⬆   Britain: -38% ⬇

There has been no substantial change in the status of the Large Skipper in the 2000–04 period.

The northward range expansion seen since the 1970s has not been discernible within the current period alone. A few new 10km squares have been recorded at the butterfly's range margin in southern Scotland, but other squares occupied in the late 1990s have no current records. These minor changes probably reflect low levels of recording rather than genuine shifts in the butterfly's distribution.

Population data add weight to the feeling that northward expansion has paused in recent years. Although the population trend of the Large Skipper shows a small increase over the long-term, transect counts were below average in each year of the 2000–04 period and the 10-year trend indicates a significant decrease on levels in the mid-1990s.

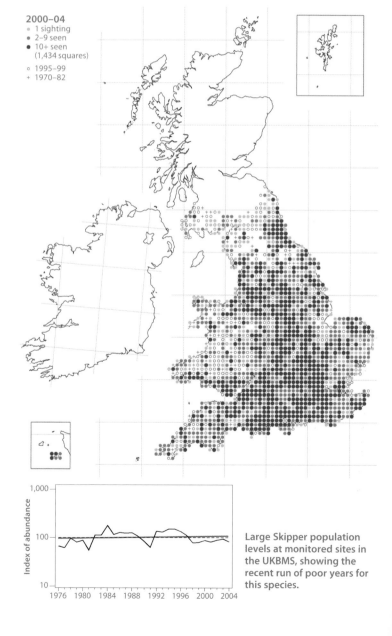

2000–04
- 1 sighting
- 2–9 seen
- 10+ seen
  (1,434 squares)
o 1995–99
+ 1970–82

Large Skipper population levels at monitored sites in the UKBMS, showing the recent run of poor years for this species.

Dingy Skipper
Erynnis tages

UK BIODIVERSITY ACTION PLAN STATUS
Candidate Priority Species

DISTRIBUTION TREND (1970–82 vs 1995–2004)
Britain: -48% ⬇   Ireland: Stable ▪

POPULATION TREND
Long-term (1976–2004)   10-year (1995–2004)
Britain: -37% ⬇   Britain: -26% ⬇

The Dingy Skipper is in decline. Its population levels were below the long-term average in every year of the 2000–04 period. Three of the five worst years since monitoring began occurred in this period, with 2001 being a particularly bad year for the butterfly. The 10-year population trend indicates an accelerating population decline.

Some colonies have become extinct since the 1995–99 survey (e.g. in south-west Scotland). Nevertheless, new colonies continue to be found, for example in western Ireland, Norfolk, and on brownfield land in north-east England, the East Midlands and West Midlands. New colonies have even been discovered in Scotland, where the Dingy Skipper is one of the rarest butterfly species. Most of these finds are attributed to increased recording effort rather than colonisation by the butterfly.

Since the 1970s, the species has undergone such considerable distribution and population declines that it now meets the criteria for inclusion as a Priority Species in the UK BAP. The increasing reliance of the species on brownfield sites in several regions adds to the conservation concern. Many such sites are under threat from redevelopment or landscaping with mown grass and planted trees, or simply from natural succession to woodland. Even if sites are secure, maintaining suitable early-successional habitats presents a serious conservation challenge.

References: Gutiérrez 2005, Wainwright 2005

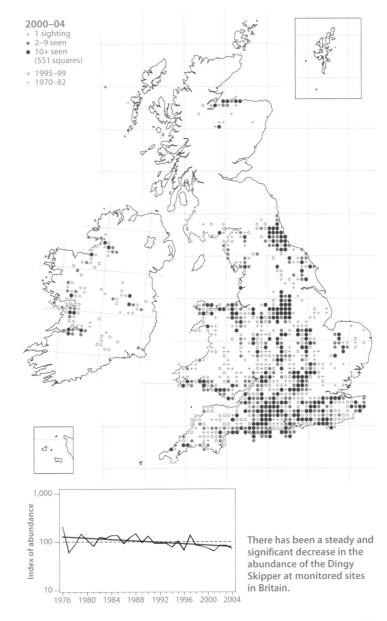

2000–04
- 1 sighting
- 2–9 seen
- 10+ seen
  (551 squares)
- 1995–99
+ 1970–82

There has been a steady and significant decrease in the abundance of the Dingy Skipper at monitored sites in Britain.

Grizzled Skipper
Pyrgus malvae

UK BIODIVERSITY ACTION PLAN STATUS
Candidate Priority Species

DISTRIBUTION TREND (1970–82 vs 1995–2004)
Britain: -49% ⬇

POPULATION TREND
Long-term (1976–2004)   10-year (1995–2004)
Britain: -34% ⬇   Britain: -42% ⬇

The fortunes of the Grizzled Skipper continued to deteriorate during the 2000–04 period. Population levels were well below the long-term average in each year except for 2002, when the species seemed to do well. Extinctions were documented for some colonies known in the 1970–82 or 1995–99 periods. For example, the species has been lost from central Lincolnshire since the 1995–99 survey.

At the same time, previously unknown colonies continue to be discovered by diligent recording, even in areas where the Grizzled Skipper is scarce, for example in Herefordshire, Norfolk and Shropshire.

The long-term declines of the Grizzled Skipper's distribution and abundance make the species a candidate for Priority Species status in the UK BAP.

Like the Dingy Skipper, many remaining Grizzled Skipper colonies are on brownfield sites, where they are threatened by successional change, redevelopment and landscaping. Conserving the butterfly in these habitats poses a considerable challenge for the future.

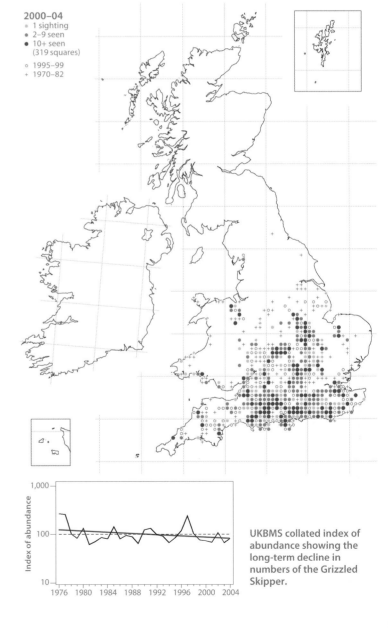

2000–04
- 1 sighting
- 2–9 seen
- 10+ seen
  (319 squares)
∘ 1995–99
+ 1970–82

UKBMS collated index of abundance showing the long-term decline in numbers of the Grizzled Skipper.

Swallowtail
Papilio machaon

UK BIODIVERSITY ACTION PLAN STATUS
Species of Conservation Concern

DISTRIBUTION TREND (1970–82 vs 1995–2004)
Britain: -5% ⬇

POPULATION TREND
Britain: insufficient data

There has been no substantial change in the status of the Swallowtail in the 2000–04 period, and it remains a rare resident species. The reintroduction trials at Wicken Fen, which were ongoing during the 1995–99 period, failed and the native *britannicus* race of the Swallowtail was recorded only in and around the Norfolk Broads in the current period.

Immigrant individuals of the *gorganus* race, which is widespread in continental Europe, were recorded rarely but widely across southern England during 2000–04 and more frequently in the Channel Islands, particularly on Jersey. Here there were several records of more than one butterfly, possibly the result of local breeding, and of larvae feeding on Fennel (*Foeniculum vulgare*) and Garden Parsley (*Petroselinum crispum*). There were also records of Swallowtail larvae on Fennel in Kent in 2000 and Suffolk in 2004, but the origin of these is unclear. It is possible that they originated from immigrant Swallowtails, but there is also the possibility of releases of captive stock.

Although continued climate warming may enable the establishment of temporary breeding colonies (and possibly eventual colonisation) by the continental Swallowtail, the future of the *britannicus* race will require ongoing concerted conservation action. Colonies have flourished in the Broads in recent decades, as a result of conservation organisations extending and managing the open fenland habitat used by the butterfly.

2000–04
- 1 sighting
- 2–9 seen
- 10+ seen (56 squares)
○ 1995–99
+ 1970–82

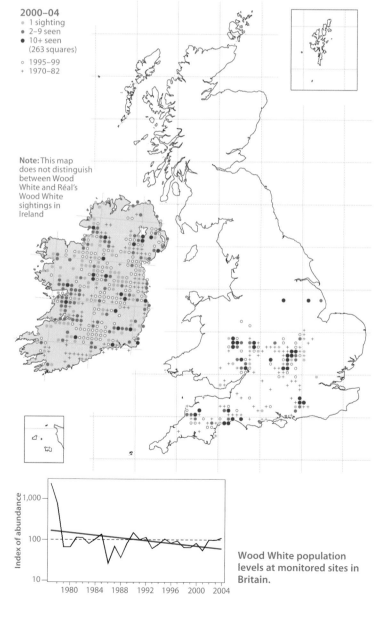

Wood White
Leptidea sinapis

UK BIODIVERSITY ACTION PLAN STATUS
Candidate Priority Species

DISTRIBUTION TREND (1970–82 vs 1995–2004)
Britain: -65% ⬇   Ireland: insufficient data

POPULATION TREND
Long-term (1977–2004)   10-year (1995–2004)
Britain: -64% ⬇   Britain: +10% ⬆

The Wood White has declined rapidly in Britain over the past few decades. Its distribution and population level declines since the 1970s make the butterfly a clear candidate for Priority Species status in the UK BAP.

Although the 2000–04 survey provides little evidence of substantial recovery at the national scale, there are some grounds for optimism. Population levels at monitored sites recovered to the long-term average in 2002 and the 10-year trend shows a small increase. In Surrey, for example, the few remaining populations increased in numbers (including large second broods in 2003 and 2004) thanks to active ride-edge management, and dispersing adults were recorded egg-laying at new sites. The Wood White has responded favourably to habitat management in Herefordshire, Shropshire and Warwickshire, and also fared well on the undercliffs of south Devon. Furthermore, it was rediscovered in south Wales in 2001. Ongoing releases make the interpretation of short-term change difficult (whilst also contributing little to the conservation of the butterfly). Records from north of The Wash are all believed to be of released Wood Whites, as are the records in Hertfordshire and Dorset.

In Ireland, our knowledge of the Wood White's distribution underwent a major change in 2001, with the discovery there of Réal's Wood White. It is now known that Réal's Wood White is by far the more common of the two visually indistinguishable species. At present, the only Irish records that have been confirmed as Wood White (from both current and historical periods) are from the limestone pavements of County Clare (Burren and adjacent areas) and to the north in County Galway (shown on the Réal's Wood White map). The precise ecological requirements of the Wood White in Ireland now require re-examination and further study.

References: Jeffcoate 2006, Nelson et al. 2001

2000–04
- 1 sighting
- 2–9 seen
- 10+ seen (263 squares)
○ 1995–99
+ 1970–82

Note: This map does not distinguish between Wood White and Réal's Wood White sightings in Ireland

Wood White population levels at monitored sites in Britain.

Réal's Wood White
Leptidea reali

UK BIODIVERSITY ACTION PLAN STATUS
Not listed

DISTRIBUTION TREND (1970–82 vs 1995–2004)
Ireland: Medium decrease ⬇

This species was unknown in the area covered by the Butterflies for the New Millennium survey until 2001, when it was discovered in Ireland. Since then, the genitalia of over 150 recent and historic specimens of 'wood white' butterflies from both Britain and Ireland have been examined to (re)determine their identity. All of the British specimens have proved to be Wood White, as had always been assumed, but specimens from much of Ireland turned out to be Réal's Wood White. Thus, the widespread distribution of 'wood whites' in both the Republic of Ireland and Northern Ireland, and the apparent northward expansion in the 1970s and 80s, both relate to Réal's Wood White. There is now a clear reason for the formerly perplexing differences in ecological requirements between Irish and British 'wood whites'.

Interestingly, the distribution of confirmed specimens thus far suggests that there is no overlap between the ranges of the two closely related species: all the specimens from the scrubby woodland of the Burren and adjoining areas are Wood White and all those from elsewhere are Réal's Wood White (see map).

As was correctly noted in *The Millennium Atlas* (albeit for the wrong *Leptidea* species!) the butterfly was significantly under-recorded in Ireland in the 1995–99 period. The current survey has added over 100 10km squares to the known distribution across the whole of Ireland. Réal's Wood White is widespread, but is probably declining in many areas due to agricultural improvement, insensitive roadside management and heavier traffic on minor roads. It seems to have disappeared from areas such as south County Cork, north County Dublin and County Meath. Such is the concern about the butterfly in Northern Ireland that is has been listed as a Priority Species there.

References: Freese and Fiedler 2002, Heal 1965, Nelson *et al.* 2001

1900–2005
· Undetermined
● Wood White
● Réal's Wood White

Clouded Yellow
Colias croceus

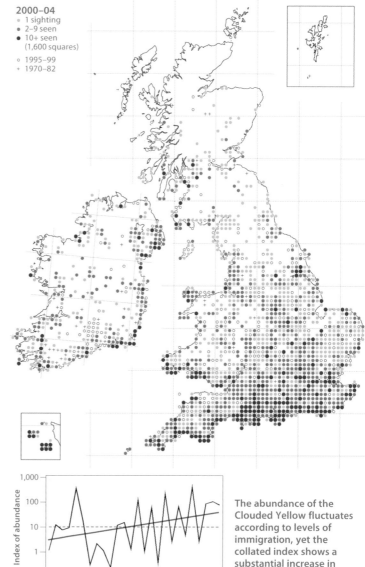

UK BIODIVERSITY ACTION PLAN STATUS
Not listed

DISTRIBUTION TREND (1970–82 vs 1995–2004)
Britain: +144% ⬆   Ireland: Increase ⬆

POPULATION TREND
Long-term (1979–2004)   10-year (1995–2004)
Britain: +1,117% ⬆   Britain: +1,877% ⬆

There was no change in the Clouded Yellow's status during the 2000–04 period; it remains a common immigrant species, capable of breeding here during the warmer months. However, it was seen in above average numbers in each year except 2001. 2000 was a great year for Clouded Yellows, with the highest population level since monitoring began in 1976 and considerably more 10km square records than in any other year of the 1995–2004 period. Clouded Yellows were seen widely across Scotland in 2000. In contrast, 1999 and 2001 were poor years, demonstrating that the annual abundance and distribution of the butterfly is determined by factors beyond our shores.

As during the 1995–99 period, the most significant observations during the current survey related to successful overwintering. Winter observations of Clouded Yellow larvae, followed by early sightings of adults at the same locations, continued during 2000–04 at a coastal site near Bournemouth, Dorset. There were also suggestions that the species might have overwintered on the Isle of Wight and in Surrey.

The Clouded Yellow's distribution and population trends strongly suggest that this migrant has become considerably more common and widespread since the 1970s, probably due to climate change.

References: Skelton 2003, Sparks *et al.* 2005

2000–04
- 1 sighting
- 2–9 seen
- 10+ seen (1,600 squares)
- 1995–99
- + 1970–82

The proportion of 10km squares in which the Clouded Yellow was recorded each year in Britain and Ireland (1995–2004).

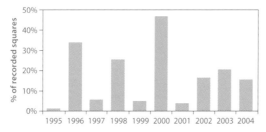

The abundance of the Clouded Yellow fluctuates according to levels of immigration, yet the collated index shows a substantial increase in numbers since 1979.

Brimstone
Gonepteryx rhamni

UK BIODIVERSITY ACTION PLAN STATUS
Not listed

DISTRIBUTION TREND (1970–82 vs 1995–2004)
Britain: -3% ⬇   Ireland:
                                    Small decrease ⬇

POPULATION TREND
Long-term (1976–2004)   10-year (1995–2004)
Britain: +22% ⬆   Britain: -11% ⬇

There has been no substantial change in the status of the Brimstone during the 2000–04 survey. Numbers at monitored sites were close to average throughout the current period (2000 was the best recent year).

The butterfly's range, on the other hand, continued to expand (see map on p.78). It was recorded in many new 10km squares, particularly at the edge of its range in the Pennines and in north-east England. As the Brimstone is a very mobile butterfly that may be seen well away from breeding habitat, it is difficult to attribute these distribution increases to range expansion or simply more frequent observation of wandering individuals as a result of increased recording effort. However, it seems likely that some spread has occurred, assisted by an increased availability of the larval foodplants, Buckthorn (*Rhamnus cathartica*) and Alder Buckthorn (*Frangula alnus*), in gardens, new hedgerows and amenity planting in northern England. Further recording has extended the known distribution in Ireland considerably since *The Millennium Atlas*.

The apparent losses of this butterfly since 1995–99 may be due, in the main, to lower levels of recording in some areas or, as is the case in southern Scotland, the original records being of vagrant butterflies. In any case, the Brimstone shows no signs of significant long-term decline at the national scale from either distribution recording or population monitoring (indeed the latter indicates a small increase) and is not of conservation concern.

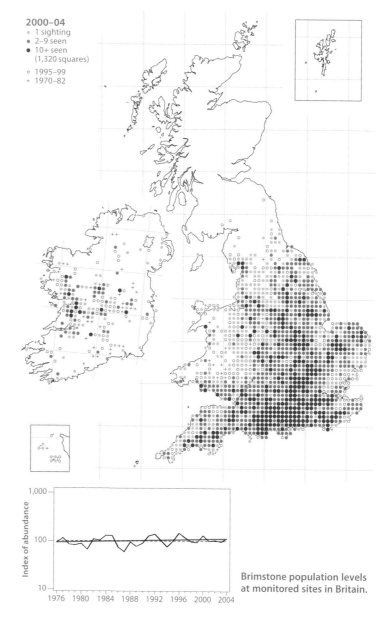

2000–04
- 1 sighting
- 2–9 seen
- 10+ seen
  (1,320 squares)
○ 1995–99
+ 1970–82

Brimstone population levels at monitored sites in Britain.

Large White
Pieris brassicae

UK BIODIVERSITY ACTION PLAN STATUS
Not listed

DISTRIBUTION TREND (1970–82 vs 1995–2004)
Britain: -7% ⬇   Ireland:
                     Small decrease ⬇

POPULATION TREND
Long-term (1976–2004)   10-year (1995–2004)
Britain: -28% ⬇   Britain: +18% ⬆

The 2000–04 survey period showed little real change for the Large White. In Ireland and northern Scotland the substantial number of new and lost 10km squares, in comparison with the 1995–99 survey, reflects under-recording in both periods as well as the migratory nature of this butterfly. The species does reach a limit to its breeding range in parts of northern Scotland (particularly away from the eastern lowlands), and here most sightings in any period are 'one off' records of wandering or migrating individuals.

Monitoring during the 2000–04 period showed that Large White populations were at or below long-term average numbers in each year, with 2001 and 2004 providing the fourth and sixth worst counts (respectively) since transects began in 1976. This run of poor years has contributed to a long-term decline at monitored sites. However, this trend is not statistically significant and the 10-year trend shows an increase as population levels have improved from a low point in 1996.

The Large White typically spends the winter in the pupal stage. However, successful larval development was observed during the winter of 2001/02 in a Nottinghamshire garden. At least one larva successfully pupated (in late March) and emerged in late April. The fact that this took place as far north as Nottinghamshire suggests that larval overwintering of the Large White may be more common nowadays than had been realised.

2000–04
- 1 sighting
- 2–9 seen
- 10+ seen
  (2,541 squares)
- ○ 1995–99
- + 1970–82

Large White population levels at monitored sites in Britain, showing the recent run of poor years for this species.

Small White
Pieris rapae

UK BIODIVERSITY ACTION PLAN STATUS
Not listed

DISTRIBUTION TREND (1970–82 vs 1995–2004)
Britain: -7% ⬇   Ireland:
                  Small decrease ⬇

POPULATION TREND
Long-term (1976–2004)   10-year (1995–2004)
Britain: +15% ⬆   Britain: -34% ⬇

There has been no substantial change in the status of this common and mobile species in the current period. Gains and losses of 10km squares since the 1995–99 survey probably reflect different patterns of recording effort in relatively under-recorded areas, as well as the wandering and migratory behaviour of the butterfly.

The Small White remains genuinely scarce through much of northern Scotland and absent as a breeding species from Shetland and the Western Isles (Outer Hebrides). Nevertheless, the butterfly was recorded from both these island groups in the current period, as well as from Orkney and from the north coast of Highland, where the Small White was once more widespread.

Population levels were low at monitored sites between 1998–2002 (resulting in a negative 10-year trend), but recovered well in 2003 and remained above the long-term average in 2004. Long-term distribution and population trends give no cause for concern.

2000–04
- 1 sighting
- 2–9 seen
- 10+ seen
  (2,397 squares)
- 1995–99
- 1970–82

Small White population levels at monitored sites in Britain.

Green-veined White
Pieris napi

UK BIODIVERSITY ACTION PLAN STATUS
Not listed

DISTRIBUTION TREND (1970–82 vs 1995–2004)
Britain: -1% ⬇   Ireland: Stable ▪

POPULATION TREND
Long-term (1976–2004)   10-year (1995–2004)
Britain: +11% ⬆   Britain: +7% ⬆

The Green-veined White is the most widespread butterfly in Britain and Ireland and there has been no recent change in its status. It was recorded in 95% of the 10km squares with records in the 1995–2004 survey, more than any other species.

There is no evidence to suggest that the species has declined in distribution recently, so the apparent losses on the map are thought to be the result of lower recording intensity in the 2000–04 survey period compared with 1995–99. Although not apparent on the map, continued BNM recording in Ireland has led to records from many new 10km squares for this species in the 2000–04 survey (particularly in Counties Donegal and Wexford). This is further evidence that past recording coverage was incomplete.

Population monitoring of the Green-veined White revealed a stable situation in the 2000–04 period and small, non-significant long-term and 10-year trends.

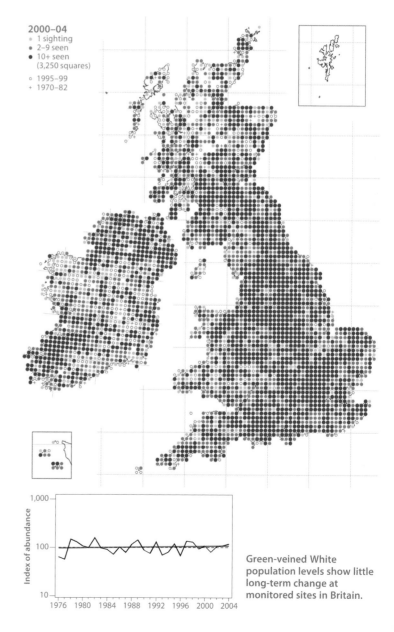

2000–04
- · 1 sighting
- ● 2–9 seen
- ● 10+ seen
  (3,250 squares)
- ○ 1995–99
- + 1970–82

Index of abundance

1,000

100

10

1976 1980 1984 1988 1992 1996 2000 2004

Green-veined White population levels show little long-term change at monitored sites in Britain.

Orange-tip
Anthocharis cardamines

UK BIODIVERSITY ACTION PLAN STATUS
Not listed

DISTRIBUTION TREND (1970–82 vs 1995–2004)
Britain: +7% ⬆   Ireland: Stable ▪

POPULATION TREND
Long-term (1976–2004)   10-year (1995–2004)
Britain: +22% ⬆   Britain: -8% ⬇

The Orange-tip fared well during 2000–04. Population levels fluctuated (2001 was the fourth worst year since 1976, yet 2002 was the fifth best), but the butterfly's distribution continued to spread northwards in Scotland (see map on p.78).

Many new 10km squares were recorded in the northern part of Argyll and across Highland, as far north as Easter Ross, but there were no confirmed records in the far north, and no repeat of the 1999 sighting in Orkney. These changes are part of an ongoing range expansion driven, we believe, by climate change.

In Ireland, Orange-tips were reported from many new 10km squares, particularly in western parts of Counties Galway and Mayo, southern County Clare and northern parts of Counties Limerick and Kerry, but it is absent from the most exposed peninsulas and islands of the west. It is likely that this increase in distribution is at least partly due to more intensive recording.

Since the 1970s, the distribution of the Orange-tip has increased in Britain and Ireland, in part due to range expansion and in part due to better recording. Somewhat surprisingly, its population levels at sites with monitoring transects have not shown the large increases seen for most butterflies with expanding ranges. This is consistent with the existence of factors, other than climate, that limit Orange-tip population density.

2000–04
- 1 sighting
- 2–9 seen
- 10+ seen (2,558 squares)
- 1995–99
- 1970–82

Orange-tip population levels show little long-term change at monitored sites in Britain.

Green Hairstreak
Callophrys rubi

UK BIODIVERSITY ACTION PLAN STATUS
Not listed

DISTRIBUTION TREND (1970–82 vs 1995–2004)
Britain: -29% ⬇   Ireland: Small decrease ⬇

POPULATION TREND
Long-term (1976–2004)   10-year (1995–2004)
Britain: -25% ⬇   Britain: -25% ⬇

The Green Hairstreak is inconspicuous and its small colonies are easily overlooked, making detailed interpretation of change difficult.

Reflecting past under-recording, volunteers found the species in new 10km squares in all parts of Britain and Ireland in 2000–04, particularly in western Ireland and in northern Scotland. It is probably still under-recorded in these areas. At the same time, many squares occupied in the 1995–99 period did not have records in the current period. In most cases this is probably due to under-recording but some colonies have been lost or are threatened with extinction, particularly on brownfield sites (for example, in the West Midlands region of England).

Population data from monitored sites provide a clearer picture of the Green Hairstreak's recent fortunes. Numbers of the butterfly were below the long-term average in every year except 2000, with 2001 and 2003 being the fourth and second (respectively) lowest population levels recorded for this species since monitoring began in 1976.

Neither the distribution nor population trends since the 1970s suggest that the Green Hairstreak merits UK BAP Priority Species status. Nevertheless, there are signs of decline, despite the continuing discovery of previously unknown colonies, and its conservation status should be kept under review.

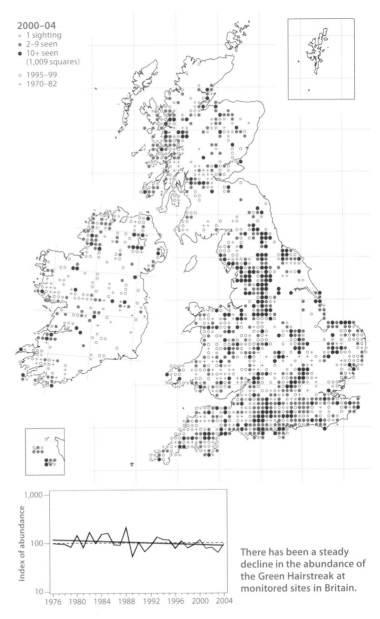

2000–04
· 1 sighting
• 2–9 seen
● 10+ seen
(1,009 squares)
○ 1995–99
+ 1970–82

There has been a steady decline in the abundance of the Green Hairstreak at monitored sites in Britain.

Brown Hairstreak
Thecla betulae

UK BIODIVERSITY ACTION PLAN STATUS
Candidate Priority Species

DISTRIBUTION TREND (1970–82 vs 1995–2004)
Britain: -43% ⬇   Ireland:
                                   Small decrease ⬇

POPULATION TREND
Britain: insufficient data

The four main strongholds of the Brown Hairstreak in Britain and Ireland remained largely intact during the 2000–04 period. Many new locations within these strongholds have been found as a result of intensive survey work by volunteers, searching for Brown Hairstreak eggs during winter. However, it is also clear that some hedges that formerly supported large numbers of eggs have been rendered completely unsuitable by repeated, severe flailing. Away from the main strongholds, there has been a substantial increase in the butterfly's known distribution to the north and east of Oxford.

This species should be easy to conserve and, following advice from Butterfly Conservation, populations have flourished at some sites as a result of less frequent hedgerow management or rotational coppicing of Blackthorn (*Prunus spinosa*) in woodlands e.g. in Lincolnshire and Worcestershire.

Efforts to integrate hedgerow management for Brown Hairstreaks into agri-environment schemes may revive the fortunes of this butterfly, provided that the measures are adopted and implemented by enough landowners. However, at present, widespread intensive flailing of hedges and neglect of woodland suggest continuing decline for the butterfly.

The distribution trend since the 1970s shows a serious decline making the butterfly a candidate for Priority Species status in the UK BAP.

Reference: Wigglesworth 2005

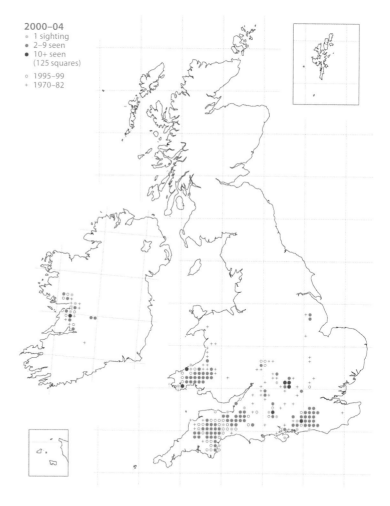

2000–04
- 1 sighting
- 2–9 seen
- 10+ seen
  (125 squares)
- 1995–99
+ 1970–82

Purple Hairstreak
Neozephyrus quercus

UK BIODIVERSITY ACTION PLAN STATUS
Not listed

DISTRIBUTION TREND (1970–82 vs 1995–2004)
Britain: -15% ⬇   Ireland: Stable ▪

POPULATION TREND
Long-term (1976–2004)   10-year (1995–2004)
Britain: +53% ⬆   Britain: -23% ⬇

Population monitoring revealed above average counts of the Purple Hairstreak in every year of the 2000–04 period, except 2004.

This canopy species is easily overlooked and lower levels of recording effort in parts of Britain during the current survey have led to apparent losses from some 10km squares. On the other hand, where special efforts have been made to survey this species in recent years, colonies have been reconfirmed or new ones found. For example, many new 10km squares have been recorded for the Purple Hairstreak in Northumberland and County Durham during 2000–04 (see map on p.78). In a few cases these reconfirmed historical records (including one site where the species was last recorded in 1896!), but most of the sightings were at new sites and there is good evidence of range expansion in this region.

Egg searching in Kent has revealed a large number of populations and new squares have also been recorded in Ireland and Scotland, where the species appears to be scarce but is probably still under-recorded. The discovery of several colonies on the south-west coastline of Highland (just to the north of Mull) extended the known range of the Purple Hairstreak by some 70km on the west coast of Scotland.

Since the 1970s, population levels of this species appear to have increased at monitored sites and the Purple Hairstreak is not a cause for conservation concern.

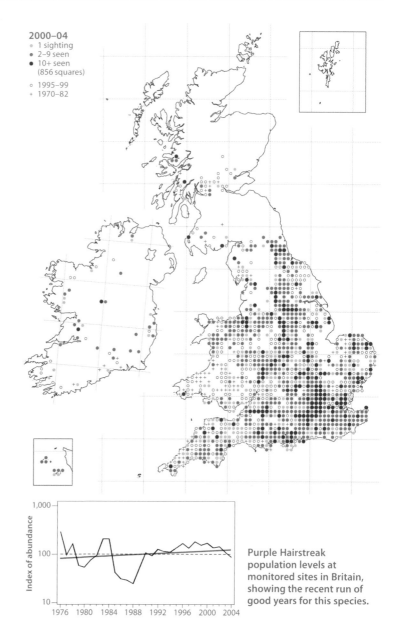

2000–04
- 1 sighting
- 2–9 seen
- 10+ seen (856 squares)
○ 1995–99
+ 1970–82

Index of abundance

1976 1980 1984 1988 1992 1996 2000 2004

Purple Hairstreak population levels at monitored sites in Britain, showing the recent run of good years for this species.

White-letter Hairstreak
Satyrium w-album

UK BIODIVERSITY ACTION PLAN STATUS
Candidate Priority Species

DISTRIBUTION TREND (1970–82 vs 1995–2004)
Britain: -53% ⬇

POPULATION TREND
Long-term (1976–2004)   10-year (1995–2004)
Britain: -71% ⬇   Britain: -63% ⬇

Although the White-letter Hairstreak did not suffer the rapid and widespread decline predicted for it at the height of Dutch Elm Disease during the 1970s and 80s, there are clear signs that this species is in trouble. A significant downward population trend, as well as the substantial distribution decrease since the 1970s, both suggest a serious decline and the species has been put forward as a candidate for Priority Species status in the UK BAP.

In the 2000–04 period, population levels at monitored sites were well below the long-term average in every year. Short-term distribution changes are more difficult to determine, as under-recording is a serious problem with this inconspicuous species. Many new 10km squares have been recorded and ones with historical records reconfirmed for the species as a result of special surveys (e.g. in Yorkshire). There is even a suggestion that the species may have spread a little in the north of England.

However, many other locations across the West Midlands and southern England have no records in the 2000–04 period, either because of losses or under-recording. The butterfly is rare in Wales, though there have been two recent records from new 10km squares in the south-west of the country.

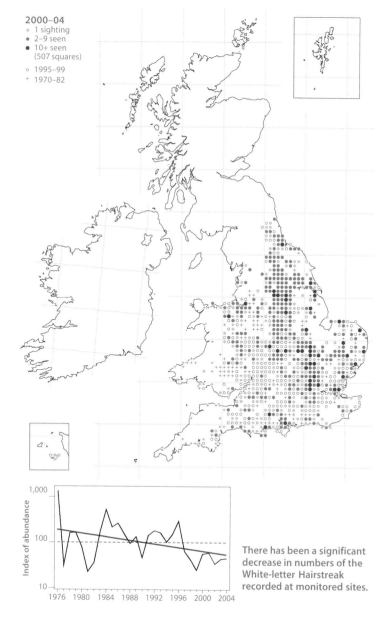

2000–04
- 1 sighting
- 2–9 seen
- 10+ seen
  (507 squares)
○ 1995–99
+ 1970–82

There has been a significant decrease in numbers of the White-letter Hairstreak recorded at monitored sites.

Black Hairstreak
Satyrium pruni

UK BIODIVERSITY ACTION PLAN STATUS
Species of Conservation Concern

DISTRIBUTION TREND (1970–82 vs 1995–2004)
Britain: -43% ⬇

POPULATION TREND
Britain: insufficient data

There has been little change at the national level in the distribution of the Black Hairstreak over the 2000–04 period and it remains a rare and elusive species. However, knowledge of the butterfly's precise distribution has improved thanks to intensive recording by local volunteers. The species appears to have been lost from several sites around Milton Keynes. In contrast, Black Hairstreaks were rediscovered at some sites with no recent records and a few 'new' colonies found (e.g. in Oxfordshire, Buckinghamshire and Cambridgeshire). The species did extremely well in 2004, with high counts at regularly recorded localities. The recent records from Lincolnshire relate to a release of captive stock.

Conservation management (coppicing or hedge-laying on a long rotation) at some sites has increased available habitat and led to increases in Black Hairstreak populations. Nevertheless, many colonies are restricted to very small breeding areas and remain vulnerable to extinction, perhaps even as a result of poor weather during the butterfly's very short flight period.

The current stability of the species remains dependent on ongoing protection and management of its favoured mature Blackthorn (*Prunus spinosa*) stands.

Without more detailed recording and monitoring, it is difficult to make a reliable assessment of change for this species. The Black Hairstreak has not been proposed for UK BAP Priority Species status, but remains of conservation concern.

Reference: Hodges 2005

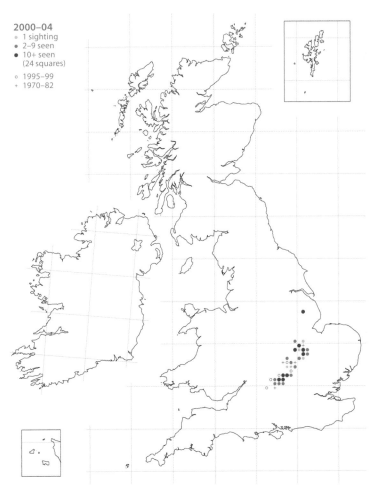

2000–04
- 1 sighting
- 2–9 seen
- 10+ seen (24 squares)
○ 1995–99
+ 1970–82

Small Copper
Lycaena phlaeas

UK BIODIVERSITY ACTION PLAN STATUS
Not listed

DISTRIBUTION TREND (1970–82 vs 1995–2004)
Britain: -16% ⬇   **Ireland:**
Medium decrease ⬇

POPULATION TREND
Long-term (1976–2004)   10-year (1995–2004)
Britain: -8% ⬇   **Britain: -41%** ⬇

The 2000–04 period brought mixed fortunes for the Small Copper. Population levels, which crashed in 1998 and 1999, initially remained at a very low ebb; 2000 and 2002 proved to be terrible years for the butterfly (the third and fourth worst since monitoring began in 1976). However, populations recovered during the hot, dry summer of 2003 and remained above the long-term average in 2004.

Although it is undoubtedly less common than it once was, particularly in intensively-managed lowland landscapes, the Small Copper is still a widespread butterfly in Britain and Ireland. Many of the apparent losses of occupied 10km squares since the 1995–99 survey are attributed to under-recording.

The Small Copper's long-term population and distribution trends in Britain do not give grounds for alarm; however, more recent population monitoring data suggest that the species is in decline. Whether this will prove to be another temporary dip in the butterfly's fluctuating population levels or the signal of a more pervasive decline remains to be seen. The Small Copper's distribution in Ireland also shows signs of decline, and needs careful monitoring.

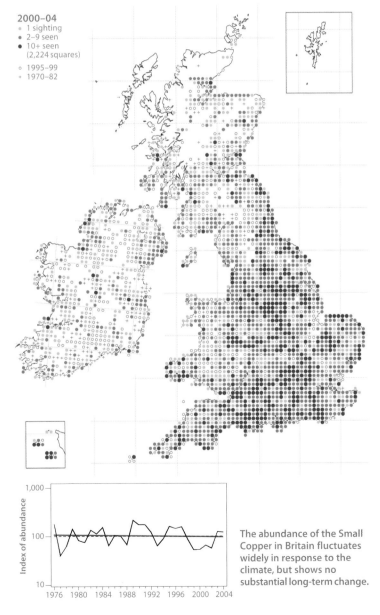

2000–04
- 1 sighting
- 2–9 seen
- 10+ seen
  (2,224 squares)
- 1995–99
+ 1970–82

The abundance of the Small Copper in Britain fluctuates widely in response to the climate, but shows no substantial long-term change.

Small Blue
Cupido minimus

UK BIODIVERSITY ACTION PLAN STATUS
Candidate Priority Species

DISTRIBUTION TREND (1970–82 vs 1995–2004)
Britain: -38% ⬇   Ireland:
                    Small decrease ⬇

POPULATION TREND
Long-term (1978–2004)   10-year (1995–2004)
Britain: -6% ⬇   Britain: +121% ⬆

Over the 2000–04 period there have been further losses of Small Blue colonies in areas already much depleted during the twentieth century. The species became extinct in Northern Ireland (last record 2001), the last remaining colony in south-east Scotland (in Borders) was lost and, despite much searching by recorders, the butterfly has not been seen in the Peak District since 1996.

Other apparent losses of 10km squares may be due to under-recording of this inconspicuous butterfly, although some colonies are undoubtedly threatened by neglect or land-use change (e.g. in Angus). In Ireland, previously unknown colonies have been discovered by intensive survey effort (e.g. along the coast of County Donegal).

The real picture of distribution change also continues to be clouded by releases. The recent record from the Morecambe Bay area is thought to be a release.

Against this background of decline, the Small Blue did well at monitored sites in 2003 and, particularly, 2004, with a good second brood, dispersal from known populations, and the establishment of new colonies (e.g. in Hampshire). Population levels in 2004 proved to be the third highest yet recorded, and the best since 1987. Such was this recovery that the butterfly's population trend, which until then had indicated a substantial decline, now suggests no long-term change.

Whilst the 10-year population trend is good news, the serious and ongoing distribution decline has led to the Small Blue being proposed for UK BAP Priority Species status.

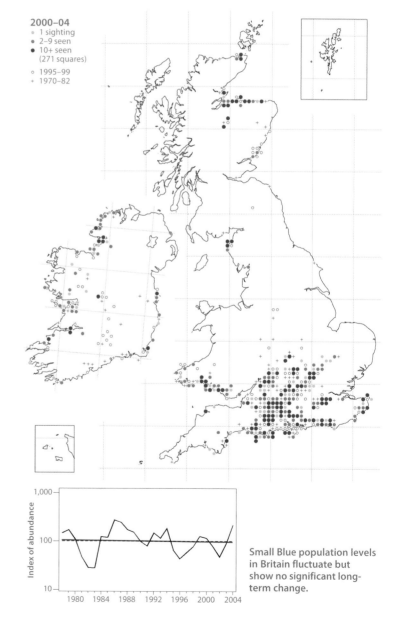

2000–04
- 1 sighting
- 2–9 seen
- 10+ seen
  (271 squares)
- 1995–99
+ 1970–82

Small Blue population levels in Britain fluctuate but show no significant long-term change.

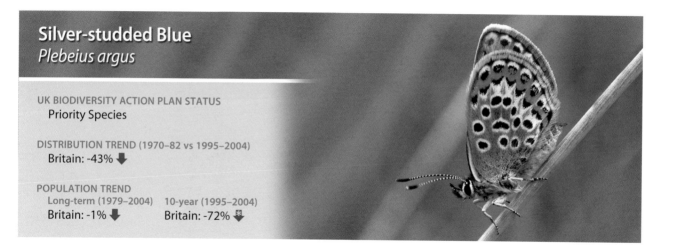

Silver-studded Blue
Plebeius argus

UK BIODIVERSITY ACTION PLAN STATUS
Priority Species

DISTRIBUTION TREND (1970–82 vs 1995–2004)
Britain: -43% ⬇

POPULATION TREND
Long-term (1979–2004)   10-year (1995–2004)
Britain: -1% ⬇   Britain: -72% ⬇

The long-term distribution decline of the Silver-studded Blue seems to have stabilised in recent years. Remaining strongholds were maintained during the 2000–04 period and the butterfly should be benefiting overall from the huge amount of heathland restoration work being undertaken across southern Britain. In addition, a successful introduction has been undertaken in north Norfolk. The record from south Yorkshire is of a release.

However, population levels at monitored sites remained below the long-term average throughout the 2000–04 period (although never falling as low as in 1999). In addition, there have been a few losses (e.g. an established introduction near Wrexham) and some isolated populations appear to be in decline (e.g. Ipswich and east Devon). There are concerns that uniform heathland management may not always produce the mosaic habitat conditions the butterfly needs.

Overall, although the species does not seem to be at risk of significant further distribution loss at present, there has been little progress towards reversing its major long-term decline. A greater focus on its habitat needs is required, even on sites with good populations. Furthermore, the 10-year population trend shows a significant and worrying decrease since the mid-1990s. The Silver-studded Blue remains a UK BAP Priority Species.

Reference: Dennis and Sparks 2006

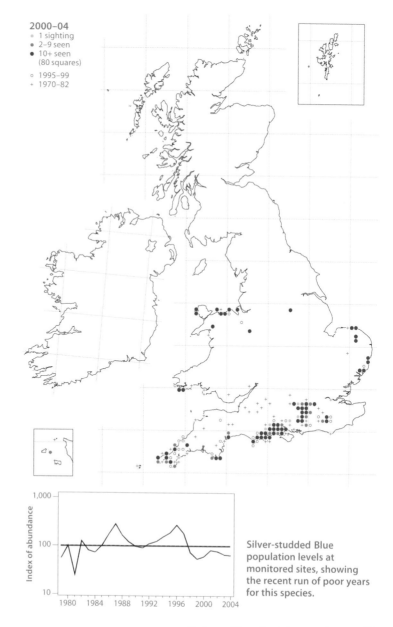

2000–04
- 1 sighting
- 2–9 seen
- 10+ seen
  (80 squares)
○ 1995–99
+ 1970–82

Silver-studded Blue population levels at monitored sites, showing the recent run of poor years for this species.

Brown Argus
Plebeius (Aricia) agestis

UK BIODIVERSITY ACTION PLAN STATUS
Not listed

DISTRIBUTION TREND (1970–82 vs 1995–2004)
Britain: +16% ⬆

POPULATION TREND

Long-term (1976–2004)	10-year (1995–2004)
Britain: +16% ⬆	Britain: -61% ⬇

The distribution of the Brown Argus increased considerably during the 2000–04 survey, even though population levels changed little over the same period at monitored sites (the best year being 2000).

In 2000–04, the butterfly colonised large parts of the East Midlands and south and east Yorkshire, reaching the North York Moors (see map on p.79). In Yorkshire and in the Peak District, this expanding front of butterflies from the south is on the verge of meeting relic populations of Brown Argus and/or Brown Argus/Northern Brown Argus hybrids (as some of the Peak District and north Yorkshire populations are believed to be) left over from range contraction in the distant past. These relic populations (and those in north Wales) are restricted to Common Rock-rose (*Helianthemum nummularium*) on calcareous habitats, but the invaders from the south are able to utilise more widespread foodplants such as Dove's-foot Crane's-bill (*Geranium molle*).

The number of broods per year, once thought to distinguish the Brown Argus from its close relative the Northern Brown Argus, is now understood to be an adaptive response to the local climate by the Brown Argus. As in 1999, single-brooded Brown Argus populations in the Peak District produced a second generation during the hot summer of 2003.

Since the 1970s, the Brown Argus has increased in distribution and population level (despite a recent decline from very high numbers in the mid-1990s). Protection and suitable management of calcareous grasslands is important for this species, but its spread away from such sites is likely to continue in the future, further improving the status of the Brown Argus.

References: Aagaard *et al*. 2002, Burke *et al*. 2005, C.D. Thomas *et al*. 2001a

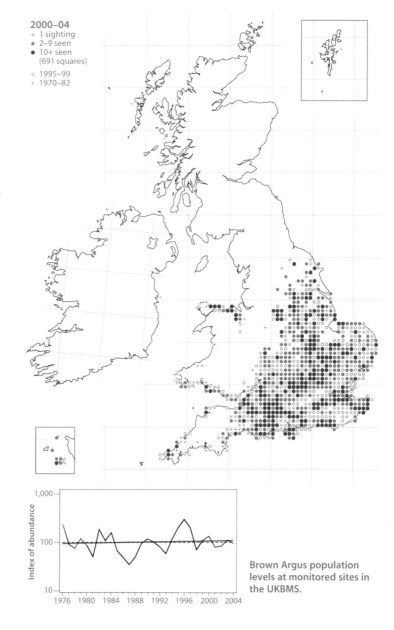

2000–04
- 1 sighting
- 2–9 seen
- 10+ seen (691 squares)
- 1995–99
+ 1970–82

Brown Argus population levels at monitored sites in the UKBMS.

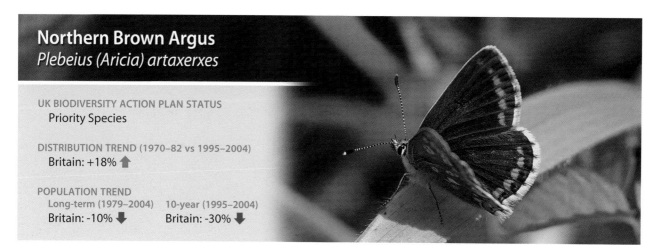

Northern Brown Argus
Plebeius (Aricia) artaxerxes

UK BIODIVERSITY ACTION PLAN STATUS
Priority Species

DISTRIBUTION TREND (1970–82 vs 1995–2004)
Britain: +18% ⬆

POPULATION TREND
Long-term (1979–2004)   10-year (1995–2004)
Britain: -10% ⬇   Britain: -30% ⬇

The distribution of the Northern Brown Argus changed little overall during the 2000–04 period. As expected, many further colonies were discovered in Scotland (particularly around the Grampian Mountains and in south-east Scotland) and north-west England as a result of continuing recording effort. Such discoveries may account for the positive long-term distribution trend.

However, population levels of this butterfly indicate a decline over the past 10 years, and counts were below average in each year of the current period. There are other worrying signs too. One of the strongest colonies in County Durham has become extinct despite apparently suitable habitat conditions and an analysis of the butterfly's metapopulation structure in north-east England questioned its long-term viability, in spite of site protection and positive conservation management. In addition, specific surveys across Britain in 2004 suggested widespread losses of both the butterfly and its foodplant Common Rock-rose (*Helianthemum nummularium*).

Genetic research during the period concluded that the Northern Brown Argus is not endemic to Britain, but is the same species as occurs in Scandinavia. There was also little evidence to justify the division of Britain's populations into subspecies.

References: Aagaard *et al*. 2002, Ellis 2003, Franco *et al*. in press, Wilson *et al*. 2002

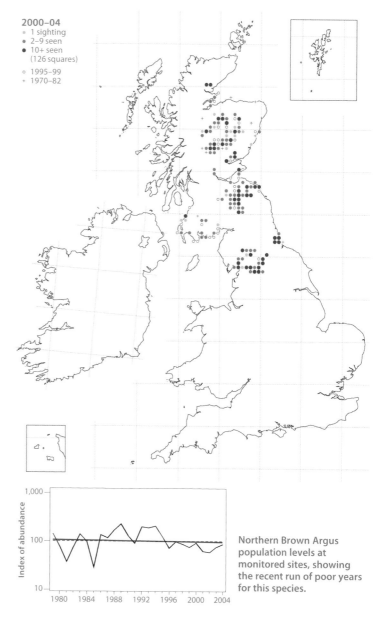

2000–04
- 1 sighting
- 2–9 seen
- 10+ seen
 (126 squares)
○ 1995–99
+ 1970–82

Northern Brown Argus population levels at monitored sites, showing the recent run of poor years for this species.

Common Blue
Polyommatus icarus

UK BIODIVERSITY ACTION PLAN STATUS
Not listed

DISTRIBUTION TREND (1970–82 vs 1995–2004)
Britain: -15% ⬇   Ireland: Small decrease ⬇

POPULATION TREND
Long-term (1976–2004)   10-year (1995–2004)
Britain: +9% ⬆   Britain: -21% ⬇

The Common Blue remains widespread and, although there is some evidence of decline at a local scale, distribution and population trends do not merit priority conservation action. There are few 10km squares with 1970s records that do not also have records from 1995–2004.

In the 2000–04 period, 2003 proved to be a good year for the Common Blue, with high population levels at monitored sites. However, counts in the preceding years were at or below average, and numbers decreased again in 2004.

In terms of distribution, the current period saw the discovery of the Common Blue in many new 10km squares in Scotland and Ireland, as well as many apparent losses, suggesting under-recording in these areas in all survey periods.

The Common Blue continues to face threats from habitat loss and deterioration (e.g. from agricultural abandonment and possibly eutrophication) and its status should be monitored closely as an indicator of the state of biodiversity in the wider countryside.

2000–04
- 1 sighting
- 2–9 seen
- 10+ seen (2,492 squares)
- 1995–99
- 1970–82

Common Blue population levels in Britain fluctuate but show little long-term change.

Chalkhill Blue
Polyommatus coridon

UK BIODIVERSITY ACTION PLAN STATUS
Species of Conservation Concern

DISTRIBUTION TREND (1970–82 vs 1995–2004)
Britain: -36% ⬇

POPULATION TREND
Long-term (1976–2004)   10-year (1995–2004)
Britain: +31% ⬆   Britain: -34% ⬇

In contrast to its close relative the Adonis Blue, the Chalkhill Blue seems to be faring rather badly at present, with a population decrease of a third over the last 10 years.

Despite reaching its highest population levels yet recorded in 1996, 1997 and 1999, numbers at monitored sites crashed in 2000–02. The 10-year trend reflects this decline, which was probably caused by the weather. There was a welcome resurgence during the hot summer of 2003, and some spectacular records of dispersing individuals tens of kilometres away from known colonies (e.g. in Essex, Suffolk and Somerset). However, this improvement was short-lived and counts were back below the long-term average in 2004.

The map probably gives an overly pessimistic view of recent distribution change as many of the 2000–04 losses were of 10km squares with only single sightings of dispersing individuals (and releases) during the 1995–99 period. Nevertheless, the long-term distribution decline of the Chalkhill Blue is a matter of concern, especially given the huge conservation effort focused on its calcareous grassland habitats during the last decade.

Although it has not been proposed for UK BAP Priority Species status there is a need for concerted conservation effort for this species.

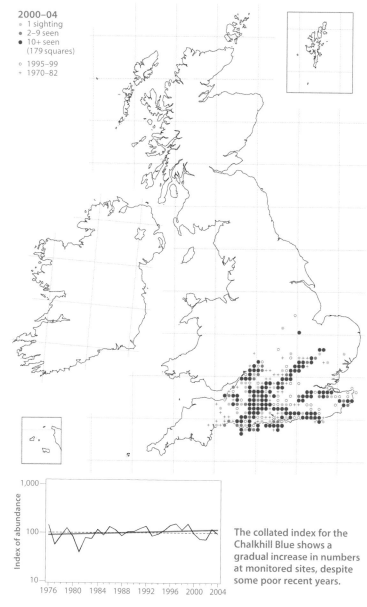

2000–04
- 1 sighting
- 2–9 seen
- 10+ seen
  (179 squares)
○ 1995–99
+ 1970–82

The collated index for the Chalkhill Blue shows a gradual increase in numbers at monitored sites, despite some poor recent years.

Adonis Blue
Polyommatus bellargus

UK BIODIVERSITY ACTION PLAN STATUS
Priority Species – proposed for downgrading to Species of Conservation Concern

DISTRIBUTION TREND (1970–82 vs 1995–2004)
Britain: -19% ⬇

POPULATION TREND
Long-term (1979–2004)   10-year (1995–2004)
Britain: +28% ⬆   Britain: +63% ⬆

The Adonis Blue increased substantially in many of its stronghold areas during 2000–04. Its population level recovered from a small dip in 2001 to the highest value yet recorded in 2003. There was a spectacularly successful second brood in 2003. At Fontmell Down in Dorset, more Adonis Blues were recorded on a single transect walk in August 2003 than the entire annual total for any other year since monitoring began there in 1980!

The butterfly's distribution changed little at the 10km square scale during the current period, but at a finer scale, significant improvements were seen. Many new sites were colonised, for example on the South Downs around Newhaven, the North Downs near Dover, and on the chalk in Wiltshire, Dorset and Hampshire. The new colonies in north Kent and Gloucestershire are thought to be the result of introductions.

Although the distribution of the butterfly has decreased since the 1970s, the recent recovery of some lost ground and, in particular, the massive increase in population levels at monitored sites since the mid-1990s have resulted in the Adonis Blue being proposed for downgrading from Priority Species to Species of Conservation Concern in the UK BAP review.

However, the species should still be considered to be highly dependent upon active conservation; whilst warmer weather may have been the catalyst for its improving status, the butterfly has only been able to respond because of the protection and appropriate management of its chalk grassland habitats. Recent research has suggested that management regimes for this species should be revised in light of climate change.

References: Bourn and Thomas 2002, Roy and Thomas 2003

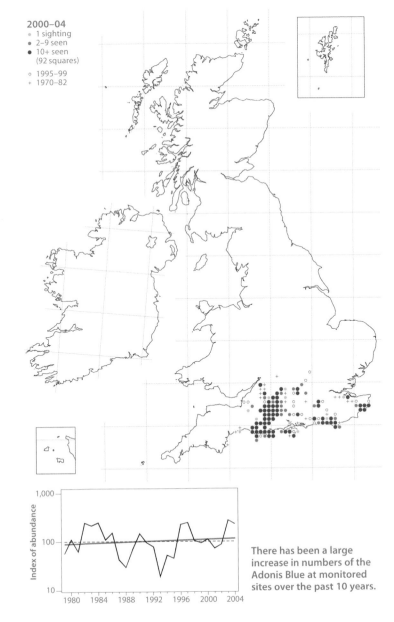

2000–04
- 1 sighting
- 2–9 seen
- 10+ seen (92 squares)
- 1995–99
+ 1970–82

There has been a large increase in numbers of the Adonis Blue at monitored sites over the past 10 years.

Holly Blue
Celastrina argiolus

UK BIODIVERSITY ACTION PLAN STATUS
Not listed

DISTRIBUTION TREND (1970–82 vs 1995–2004)
Britain: +36% ⬆   Ireland: Increase ⬆

POPULATION TREND
Long-term (1976–2004)   10-year (1995–2004)
Britain: +281% ⬆   Britain: -30% ⬇

The Holly Blue began the 2000–04 period at the lowest point of its population cycle (although this was not as low as in previous monitored cycles) and numbers grew to a peak in spring 2002. A decrease in 2003 looked to be the start of another downward cycle but, instead, populations increased in 2004, with particularly high counts in the summer generation.

Distribution records once again mirrored this cycle, with the greatest number of 10km squares recorded in 2002 and 2004. Holly Blues were recorded in southern Scotland in both of these good years.

In Ireland, where the species has a more fragmented distribution, many new 10km squares were recorded in the current survey, particularly in County Donegal and in the 'heat island' of urban Dublin. As well as being recorded more widely, the Holly Blue is also changing its phenology in Ireland, presumably in response to the warming climate. A small second brood has been reported in Northern Ireland from 2001 onwards and there was a partial third brood in and around the cities of Dublin and Cork from 2002 to 2004.

Despite its familiar 'boom and bust' population cycles, there is clear long-term evidence of increasing population levels and a northward spread of the Holly Blue (see map on p.79).

Reference: Aldwell and Nash 2005

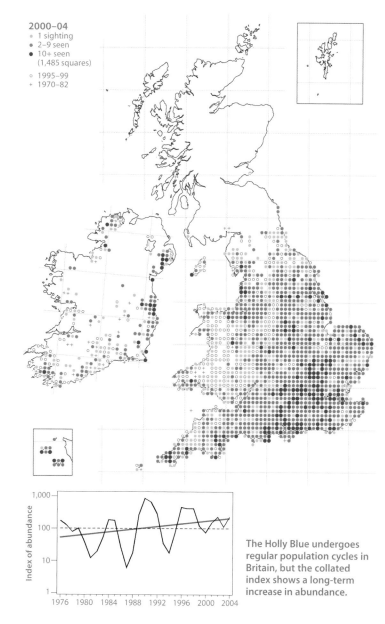

2000–04
- 1 sighting
- 2–9 seen
- 10+ seen
  (1,485 squares)
○ 1995–99
+ 1970–82

The Holly Blue undergoes regular population cycles in Britain, but the collated index shows a long-term increase in abundance.

Large Blue
Glaucopsyche (Maculinea) arion

UK BIODIVERSITY ACTION PLAN STATUS
Priority Species

DISTRIBUTION TREND (1970–82 vs 1995–2004)
Britain: extinction and successful re-establishment

POPULATION TREND
Britain: extinction and successful re-establishment

The re-establishment programme continued successfully in the 2000–04 period, and the Large Blue flew on 10 sites in 2004 (shown at 10km square resolution on the map).

Successes in the current period include the establishment of a small population in the Cotswolds, Gloucestershire (where earlier attempts had failed), the first reintroduction on the north coast of Cornwall and the creation of a colony at a site with public access; the National Trust's Collard Hill in Somerset. Details of how to visit the latter site can be found at www.butterfly-conservation.org or www.nationaltrust.org.uk.

The butterfly has continued to survive at the Devon site where the Large Blue was first reintroduced to Britain in 1983 and populations are stable or increasing at all of the sites in the Polden Hills (Somerset). There is even evidence of spread from a few introduction sites to nearby restored habitat.

Although it has required a huge effort by a large number of individuals and organisations, the Large Blue is probably now present in greater numbers in Britain than at any time in the last 50 years. This is a considerable achievement for a globally endangered species that is in steep decline across continental Europe.

The number of restored colonies of the Large Blue 1983–2004 (data courtesy of the Centre for Ecology and Hydrology).

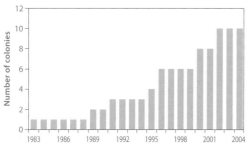

2004
- 1 sighting
- 2–9 seen
- 10+ seen (5 squares)
+ 1970–82

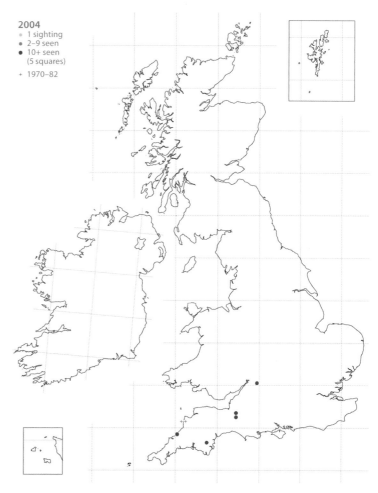

Duke of Burgundy
Hamearis lucina

UK BIODIVERSITY ACTION PLAN STATUS
Candidate Priority Species

DISTRIBUTION TREND (1970–82 vs 1995–2004)
Britain: -52% ⬇

POPULATION TREND
Long-term (1979–2004)   **10-year (1995–2004)**
Britain: -28% ⬇   **Britain: -58%** ⬇

The Duke of Burgundy is in serious decline. Long-term distribution and population trends are very worrying and the butterfly has been proposed as a candidate Priority Species for the UK BAP.

The 2000–04 period provided evidence of further decline. Population levels decreased in every year and, by 2004, had reached the lowest point yet recorded. The species fared badly in northern England, particularly on the Morecambe Bay Limestones, where it was recorded at only 11 sites. In Yorkshire, the butterfly's response to recent conservation management at some of the 20 remaining sites has been disappointing and further extinctions are expected. Two new 10km square records in northern England (one in Lancashire and the other close to the Yorkshire coast) are thought to be releases. The species has become extinct in Surrey, and there have been many losses of colonies elsewhere (e.g. in Dorset, Sussex, the Polden Hills in Somerset and the Cotswolds in Gloucestershire).

The Duke of Burgundy cannot tolerate high levels of grazing and seems to have suffered during the restoration and intensive management of some calcareous grasslands. A more flexible approach to such management is required, recognising the threat to species such as the Duke of Burgundy and Small Blue. At the other end of the management spectrum, neglect has also been a problem, with woodland and grassland colonies driven to extinction by excessive shading of larval foodplants.

Most remaining colonies are small and isolated and the 10-year population trend shows a significant decline; the future looks bleak for this butterfly. Urgent efforts are needed at the landscape scale to combat fragmentation and to develop suitable management regimes to meet the butterfly's mosaic habitat requirements.

Reference: Oates 2000

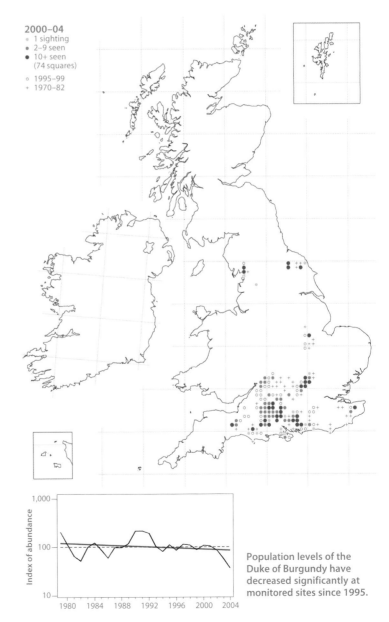

2000–04
- 1 sighting
- 2–9 seen
- 10+ seen
  (74 squares)
- 1995–99
- 1970–82

Population levels of the Duke of Burgundy have decreased significantly at monitored sites since 1995.

White Admiral
Limenitis camilla

UK BIODIVERSITY ACTION PLAN STATUS
Candidate Priority Species

DISTRIBUTION TREND (1970–82 vs 1995–2004)
Britain: -31% ⬇

POPULATION TREND
Long-term (1976–2004)   10-year (1995–2004)
Britain: -62% ⬇   Britain: -36% ⬇

Population levels of the White Admiral have plummeted at monitored sites. The long-term trend shows a significant decrease, resulting in proposed UK BAP Priority Species status, and the rate of population decline seems to have increased since the mid-1990s. 2002 was the worst year for the species since monitoring started in 1976, and 2001 was the third poorest. 2003 and 2004 brought welcome improvements, with numbers almost back to the long-term average, but it remains to be seen whether this increase can be sustained.

The distribution trend of this woodland butterfly also shows a considerable decline since the 1970s. However, this trend belies evidence of northward range expansion (see map on p.79). There was further colonisation in 2000–04, particularly in East Anglia, Leicestershire and Lincolnshire. Sadly, the pattern of range change is clouded by releases, as well as by the natural wanderings of White Admirals. The origin of individuals recorded in Cheshire and Yorkshire is unclear.

The current period also included some extraordinary records of second brood (September/October) individuals of this normally strictly univoltine species. 2003 provided the greatest number of sightings, with records from the northern edge of the species range (e.g. Norfolk, Rutland and Warwickshire) as well as from southern counties. Sightings were also reported in 2002 (Buckinghamshire) and 2004 (Essex, Norfolk and Suffolk).

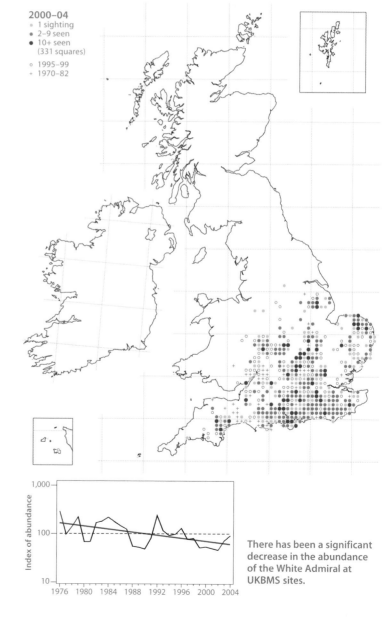

2000–04
- 1 sighting
- 2–9 seen
- 10+ seen
  (331 squares)
- 1995–99
- 1970–82

There has been a significant decrease in the abundance of the White Admiral at UKBMS sites.

Purple Emperor
Apatura iris

UK BIODIVERSITY ACTION PLAN STATUS
Species of Conservation Concern

DISTRIBUTION TREND (1970–82 vs 1995–2004)
Britain: -52% ⬇

POPULATION TREND
Long-term (1979–2004)   10-year (1995–2004)
Britain: -18% ⬇   Britain: +33% ⬆

There does not appear to have been any major change in the status of the Purple Emperor during the 2000–04 period, although the species appeared to have poor years in 2002 and 2004, and a very good year in 2003.

The difficulty of monitoring this butterfly of the woodland canopy makes under-recording a real problem. Whilst an absence of records for a decade or more might reasonably be regarded as colony extinction for most butterfly species, the same cannot be assumed for the Purple Emperor. As a consequence, the distribution trend may not be a good estimate of species status change in this case.

Dedicated survey work during the current period by volunteers across the butterfly's range suggested little evidence of decline in core areas. For example, by looking at the tree tops (often from outside the wood) and checking suitable 'master trees' or 'assembly areas' that might be used by the butterflies, volunteers in Hertfordshire and north London rediscovered Purple Emperors in many woods with no recent records. One very active assembly area, discovered in 2004, was located within 100m of the site car park, an environment centre, a public road and private gardens, yet the only previous Purple Emperor report from the wood was in 1966!

Without more detailed recording and monitoring, it is difficult to make a reliable assessment of change for this butterfly. The Purple Emperor has not been proposed for UK BAP Priority Species status, but remains of conservation concern.

Reference: Oates *et al.* 2005

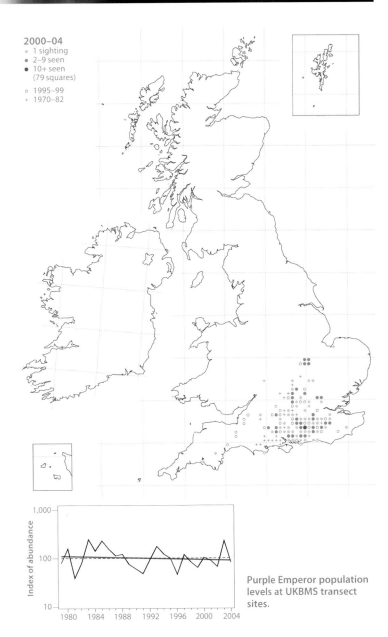

2000–04
- 1 sighting
- 2–9 seen
- 10+ seen (79 squares)
- 1995–99
+ 1970–82

Purple Emperor population levels at UKBMS transect sites.

Red Admiral
Vanessa atalanta

UK BIODIVERSITY ACTION PLAN STATUS
Not listed

DISTRIBUTION TREND (1970–82 vs 1995–2004)
Britain: +25% ⬆   Ireland: Increase ⬆

POPULATION TREND
Long-term (1976–2004)   10-year (1995–2004)
Britain: +350% ⬆   Britain: -38% ⬇

The Red Admiral continued to do well in the 2000–04 period. 2003 proved to be the second best year for the species since population monitoring began in 1976, and 2000 was also good. In contrast, 2004 was a very poor year by recent standards, and the worst since 1991. Overall, the long-term population trend shows a significant increase in numbers since the 1970s, probably due to climate change.

There was further evidence of successful overwintering by Red Admirals during the 2000–04 period. Recent observations of territorial behaviour and mating in late summer and of egg laying in November and December fit the picture of a species making a transition from a summer breeding species to a year-round resident. There has also been a big increase in winter sightings of adult Red Admirals, something that was a rare event in the 1970s. These climate-related changes are expected to continue with predicted future warming.

References: Dennis *et al*. 2006b, Sparks *et al*. 2005

2000–04
- 1 sighting
- 2–9 seen
- 10+ seen
  (2,838 squares)
○ 1995–99
+ 1970–82

There has been a massive increase in numbers of the Red Admiral at monitored sites in Britain.

Painted Lady
Vanessa cardui

UK BIODIVERSITY ACTION PLAN STATUS
Not listed

DISTRIBUTION TREND (1970–82 vs 1995–2004)
Britain: +32% ⬆   Ireland: Increase ⬆

POPULATION TREND
Long-term (1976–2004)   10-year (1995–2004)
Britain: +520% ⬆   Britain: +118% ⬆

The Painted Lady was seen in good numbers in all but one year (2001) of the current five-year survey period.

Numbers on butterfly transects were extremely high in 2003, the second highest total (after 1996) since monitoring began in 1976. It was a classic Painted Lady invasion: large numbers arrived across southern counties at the beginning of June 2003 (e.g. a sighting of over 400 in a field near Ipswich) and within a couple of days had spread across Britain and Ireland. Successful breeding and further immigration led to high numbers through the summer and autumn.

February 2004 brought another extraordinary Painted Lady immigration event, with butterflies seen, sometimes in high numbers (e.g. about 100 on the Isle of Portland, Dorset), across southern England and reaching as far north as Cumbria. An influx so early in the year is not unique, but the size of this immigration was extremely unusual.

Even with all this activity, the number and distribution of Painted Ladies in Britain and Ireland each year remains wholly dependent upon immigration from the butterfly's permanent breeding grounds in southern Europe and North Africa.

The proportion of 10km squares in which the Painted Lady was recorded each year in Britain and Ireland (1995–2004).

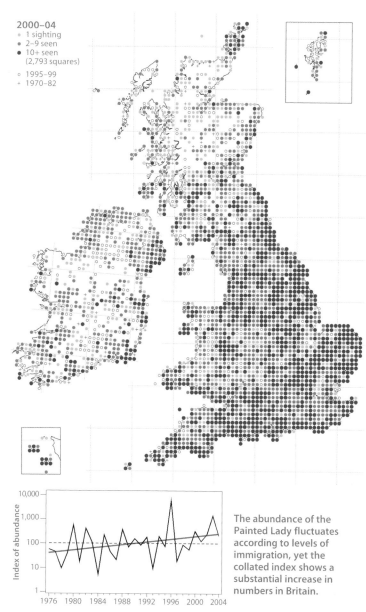

2000–04
- 1 sighting
- 2–9 seen
- 10+ seen
  (2,793 squares)
- ○ 1995–99
- + 1970–82

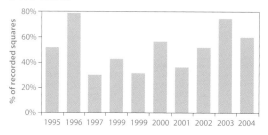

The abundance of the Painted Lady fluctuates according to levels of immigration, yet the collated index shows a substantial increase in numbers in Britain.

Small Tortoiseshell
Aglais urticae

UK BIODIVERSITY ACTION PLAN STATUS
Not listed

DISTRIBUTION TREND (1970–82 vs 1995–2004)
Britain: -3% ⬇   Ireland: Stable ■

POPULATION TREND
Long-term (1976–2004)   10-year (1995–2004)
Britain: -15% ⬇   Britain: -34% ⬇

Despite the concerns raised by some butterfly recorders, the 2000–04 period has seen no major change in the status of the Small Tortoiseshell. Indeed the species has fared rather well, recovering from its lowest recorded population level, in 1999, to a relatively high count in 2003.

As can be seen from the plot of population levels, such fluctuations appear to be normal for this species, at least since monitoring began in 1976.

The population trend suggests little long-term change in Small Tortoiseshell numbers. The butterfly remains very common in Britain and Ireland, and was the third most widely recorded species in the 2000–04 survey.

2000–04
- 1 sighting
- 2–9 seen
- 10+ seen
  (2,949 squares)
- 1995–99
- 1970–82

The abundance of the Small Tortoiseshell in Britain fluctuates widely, but the collated index shows no significant long-term change.

The distribution of the Peacock continued to expand northwards during the 2000–04 period, with a large increase in records north of the Firth of Forth. Observers in Highland noted a sudden appearance of Peacocks in September 2002 and the species now appears to have colonised many areas of northern Scotland (see map on p.79). Larvae have been reported from the Ardnamurchan and Moidart areas of the west coast and from Skye, and, in the east, from Grantown-on-Spey and near Inverness. There was also a record of a Peacock hibernating in a peat stack from Lewis in the Western Isles in 2004, which appears to be the first sighting of this species on the island.

In contrast, population levels at monitored sites declined in each year of the 2000–04 period, falling below the long-term average in 2003 and 2004. Counts in 2004 were the worst since 1986 and the sixth worst since monitoring began in 1976. The 10-year trend reflects this 'bad patch', but the butterfly has increased significantly over the long term.

The normally single-brooded Peacock produced a small second generation in recent hot summers. Larvae were found in September in Wiltshire and Essex (in 2003 and 2004 respectively) with adults emerging in early October. Although this phenomenon has been recorded occasionally in the past, it may become a more familiar occurrence if the climate warms as predicted.

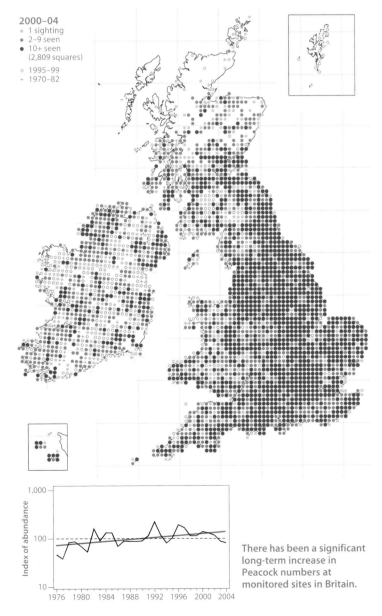

2000–04
· 1 sighting
· 2–9 seen
● 10+ seen
(2,809 squares)
○ 1995–99
+ 1970–82

There has been a significant long-term increase in Peacock numbers at monitored sites in Britain.

Comma
Polygonia c-album

UK BIODIVERSITY ACTION PLAN STATUS
Not listed

DISTRIBUTION TREND (1970–82 vs 1995–2004)
Britain: +37% ⬆

POPULATION TREND
Long-term (1976–2004)   10-year (1995–2004)
Britain: +305% ⬆   Britain: +64% ⬆

The Comma's range expansion continued in 2000–04, especially on the eastern side of Britain (see map on p.79). The butterfly was recorded in many new 10km squares in south-east Scotland, and there were also gains in the west, mainly in Cumbria, along with a few sightings in Dumfries and Galloway and one in Ayrshire. There were also two confirmed records in northern Scotland. A further sighting in Fife was thought to be due to a release.

Although there have been no reports of larvae from Scotland, it seems that the Comma is resident there once again, at least in the south-east, for the first time since c.1870.

The current survey also produced further Comma sightings from Ireland and the Isle of Man. All of these are assumed to be vagrants and there is no evidence that the butterfly has become established in these countries.

Concurrent with the ongoing range expansion (the second greatest percentage increase for a resident species), the Comma's population in Britain continued to increase. Counts at monitored sites were above the long-term average in each year (2000–04); 2003 yielded the highest levels since transects began in 1976, 2004 the third highest and 2000 the fourth highest.

The range expansion of the Comma is expected to continue in the future, driven, we believe, by climate change.

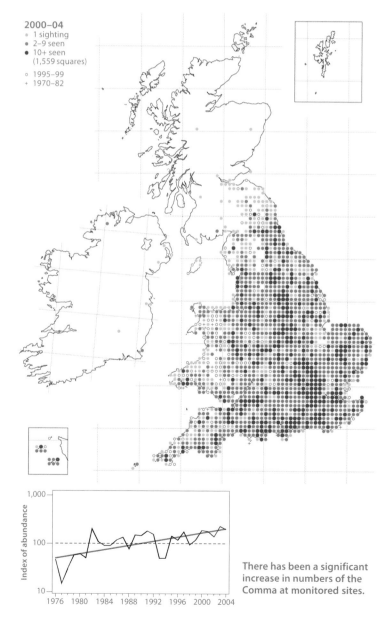

2000–04
- 1 sighting
- 2–9 seen
- 10+ seen
  (1,559 squares)
- 1995–99
+ 1970–82

There has been a significant increase in numbers of the Comma at monitored sites.

Small Pearl-bordered Fritillary
Boloria selene

UK BIODIVERSITY ACTION PLAN STATUS
Candidate Priority Species

DISTRIBUTION TREND (1970–82 vs 1995–2004)
Britain: -34% ⬇

POPULATION TREND
Long-term (1976–2004)   10-year (1995–2004)
Britain: -70% ⬇   Britain: -10% ⬇

The distribution of the Small Pearl-bordered Fritillary has continued to decline in England (especially in woodland), but the butterfly remains widespread on the wet grasslands, moors, hillsides and open woodland of western and northern Britain.

Population levels at monitored sites were very low between 2000–03, but recovered to above long-term average levels in 2004. Despite this recent improvement, the long-term trend reveals a massive decline.

The situation is particularly worrying in south-east England. The species became extinct in Kent in the 1990s (last record 1997, although this may have been a release) and has probably been lost from Surrey. The last confirmed Surrey record was in 2001, although a large number of butterflies appeared mysteriously at a well-recorded site in 2004 (presumably the result of a release). In addition, there appear to have been several losses from woodlands in West Sussex. Even in the west, there is clear evidence of decline in Dorset, Wiltshire and north-east and south-east Wales.

The ongoing loss of colonies and the significant decline in abundance at monitored sites since 1976 make the Small Pearl-bordered Fritillary a candidate for Priority Species status in the UK BAP.

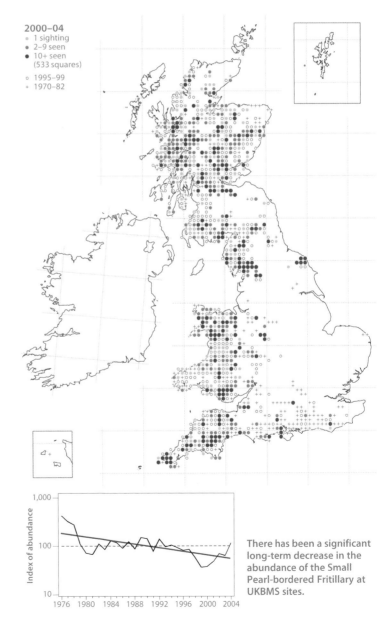

2000–04
- 1 sighting
- 2–9 seen
- 10+ seen (533 squares)
- 1995–99
+ 1970–82

There has been a significant long-term decrease in the abundance of the Small Pearl-bordered Fritillary at UKBMS sites.

Pearl-bordered Fritillary
Boloria euphrosyne

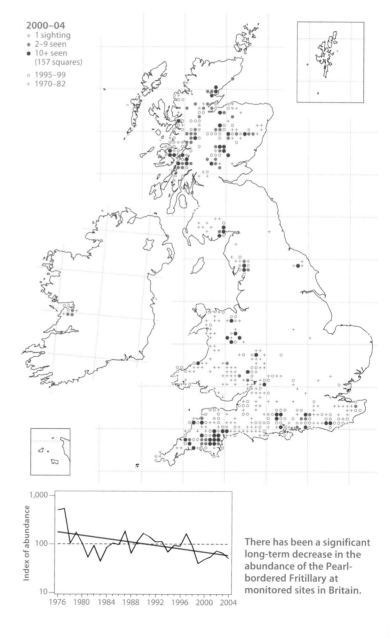

UK BIODIVERSITY ACTION PLAN STATUS
Priority Species

DISTRIBUTION TREND (1970–82 vs 1995–2004)
Britain: -61% ⬇   Ireland: insufficient data

POPULATION TREND
Long-term (1976–2004)   10-year (1995–2004)
Britain: -66% ⬇   **Britain: -51%** ⬇

Despite its Priority Species status, the Pearl-bordered Fritillary has continued to decline, especially in England and Wales. Detailed surveys revealed that a third of English colonies became extinct between 1997 and 2004, leaving perhaps only 170 surviving populations. In the south-east, 55% of colonies were lost over this seven-year period, with the main cause being a lack of appropriate woodland management.

Since 1997, the species has become extinct in Dorset, Kent and Somerset. It may also be extinct in Pembrokeshire, and has been reduced to a single colony in Surrey and a single site (with several colonies) in Gloucestershire. Even in strongholds such as Dartmoor and on the Morecambe Bay Limestones, some colonies have been lost in recent years. The butterfly remains quite widespread and probably under-recorded in Scotland and there is no evidence of decline on the scrubland habitats of western Ireland.

The long-term and 10-year population trends for the Pearl-bordered Fritillary at monitored sites show worrying declines, justifying the high level of conservation priority. There are some grounds for optimism however. Population levels remained well below average during the 2000–04 period but there was no further decline and the species did relatively well in 2002 and 2003. Furthermore, numbers have increased dramatically at some sites in response to habitat management (e.g. in Denbighshire, the Morecambe Bay area, the New Forest, West Sussex and the Wyre Forest in Shropshire/Worcestershire).

Much more conservation effort, focussed at the landscape scale, will be required to rescue the Pearl-bordered Fritillary from the brink of extinction across much of England and Wales.

Reference: Hoare 2006

2000–04
● 1 sighting
● 2–9 seen
● 10+ seen
   (157 squares)
○ 1995–99
+ 1970–82

There has been a significant long-term decrease in the abundance of the Pearl-bordered Fritillary at monitored sites in Britain.

High Brown Fritillary
Argynnis adippe

UK BIODIVERSITY ACTION PLAN STATUS
Priority Species

DISTRIBUTION TREND (1970–82 vs 1995–2004)
Britain: -79% ⬇

POPULATION TREND
Long-term (1978–2004)   10-year (1995–2004)
Britain: -13% ⬇   Britain: -85% ⬇

Since the 1970s, the High Brown Fritillary has suffered the greatest distribution decrease of any extant butterfly and is one of our most threatened butterflies. However, the species had mixed fortunes during the 2000–04 period. On the positive side, habitat management led to population increases at some sites, notably on the Morecambe Bay Limestones in north Lancashire and south Cumbria, and in the Alun Valley, the only remaining site for the butterfly in south Wales. Colonies seem to have fared reasonably well through the current period on Dartmoor too. These recoveries, aided by good weather in 2003, led to national population level increases in 2003 and 2004.

On the other hand, populations of the High Brown Fritillary have collapsed on Exmoor, with all known colonies within the National Park becoming extinct in the 2000–04 period. The picture is almost as bleak in the Malvern Hills, where the butterfly is only just hanging on despite a major conservation initiative in recent years. Most of the apparent distribution losses in the Morecambe Bay area are where vagrants were seen in the previous recording period and do not represent colony extinctions. The butterfly's 10-year population trend is the worst decline of any species!

The High Brown Fritillary remains a high priority for conservation action and its future in many areas is by no means certain. Continued effort is required at those sites where populations have responded well, and fresh impetus is needed in other areas if the species is not to be lost in the near future. For example, it is hoped that a new project focussed on the threatened fritillaries of Exmoor, which began in 2005, will help to restore the High Brown Fritillary in this former stronghold.

Population trends for this species include timed count data as well as transects. This is to ensure that the trends accurately reflect the butterfly's national population status, as most transect sites for this species are located in the Morecambe Bay area.

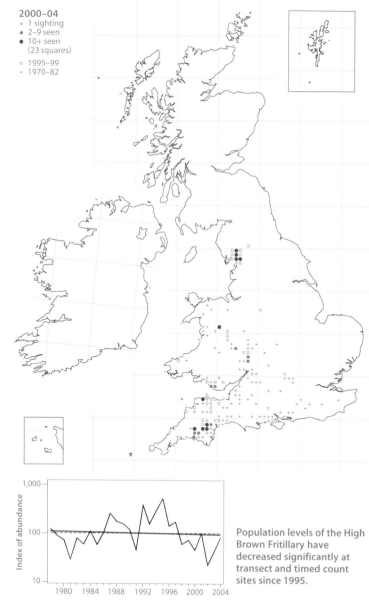

2000–04
- 1 sighting
- 2–9 seen
- 10+ seen (23 squares)
○ 1995–99
+ 1970–82

Population levels of the High Brown Fritillary have decreased significantly at transect and timed count sites since 1995.

Dark Green Fritillary
Argynnis aglaja

UK BIODIVERSITY ACTION PLAN STATUS
Not listed

DISTRIBUTION TREND (1970–82 vs 1995–2004)
Britain: -30% ⬇   Ireland:
                     Medium decrease ⬇

POPULATION TREND
Long-term (1976–2004)   10-year (1995–2004)
Britain: +63% ⬆   Britain: -10% ⬇

Distribution and population data present contrasting information on the changing status of the Dark Green Fritillary. The species remains the most widespread fritillary in Britain (though not in Ireland), but its distribution has declined considerably since the 1970s, especially in eastern England. However this decrease is not quite sufficient to merit UK BAP Priority Species status.

A short-term assessment is more difficult, and many of the recent apparent losses on the map are thought to be due either to under-recording or to the previous record being of a single, wandering individual. On the other hand, improved survey effort in other areas led to the butterfly being found in 267 new 10km squares during the 2000–04 survey (notably in northern and south-east Scotland, north-west England and along the north coast of Ireland).

Set against the long-term distribution decline, population levels of the Dark Green Fritillary have increased since the 1970s, and high counts were made at monitored sites in 2003 and 2004 (fourth and third highest levels, respectively, since 1976). Furthermore, the species seems to be spreading in some areas (e.g. Bedfordshire).

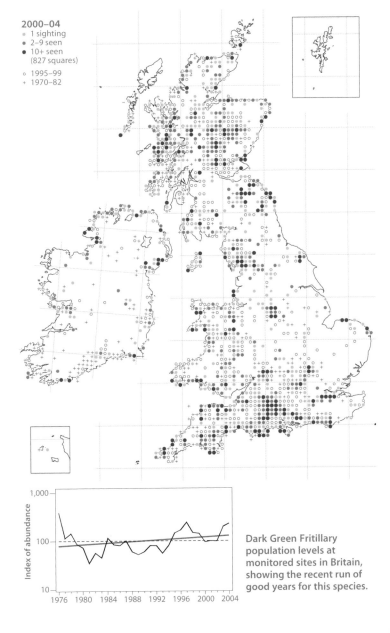

2000–04
- 1 sighting
- 2–9 seen
- 10+ seen
  (827 squares)
○ 1995–99
+ 1970–82

Index of abundance

1976 1980 1984 1988 1992 1996 2000 2004

Dark Green Fritillary population levels at monitored sites in Britain, showing the recent run of good years for this species.

Silver-washed Fritillary
Argynnis paphia

UK BIODIVERSITY ACTION PLAN STATUS
Species of Conservation Concern

DISTRIBUTION TREND (1970–82 vs 1995–2004)
Britain: -29% ⬇   Ireland:
                        Medium decrease ⬇

POPULATION TREND
Long-term (1976–2004)   10-year (1995–2004)
Britain: +33% ⬆   Britain: -14% ⬇

The status of the Silver-washed Fritillary has continued to improve during the current period against a background of long-term distribution decline. 2003 and 2004 yielded high population counts of the butterfly at monitored sites (respectively the fifth and fourth highest population levels since 1976). In addition, there were records from new 10km squares across the northern edge of the species core range in southern Britain (see map on p.79). The apparent recent losses in the East Midlands are where vagrant or released individuals had been recorded previously, and do not represent colony extinctions.

In Ireland, where this species is the most widespread fritillary, there has been a massive increase in the recorded distribution: during 2000–04, 123 new 10km squares were added to the 166 recorded in the 1995–99 survey. This is thought to be due mainly to increased recording effort.

The population and distribution trends since the 1970s do not give any serious cause for concern, but the butterfly still has a long way to go if it is to recover its historical range.

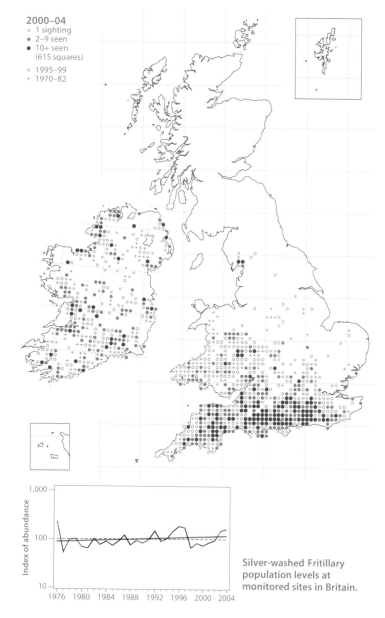

2000–04
- 1 sighting
- 2–9 seen
- 10+ seen
  (615 squares)
○ 1995–99
+ 1970–82

Silver-washed Fritillary population levels at monitored sites in Britain.

Marsh Fritillary
Euphydryas aurinia

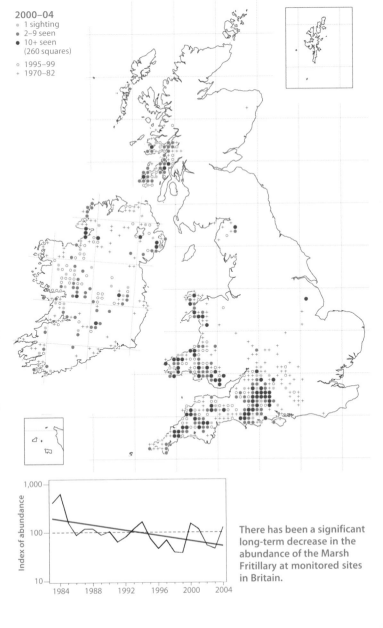

UK BIODIVERSITY ACTION PLAN STATUS
Priority Species

DISTRIBUTION TREND (1970–82 vs 1995–2004)
Britain: -46% ⬇   Ireland:
                        Severe decrease ⬇

POPULATION TREND
Long-term (1983–2004)   10-year (1995–2004)
Britain: -73% ⬇   Britain: +73% ⬆

The Marsh Fritillary's long-term decline continued during 2000–04, with particularly poor counts in 2002 and 2003. In addition to the long-term British distribution and population declines, 66% of colonies in England were lost between 1990 and 2000. The most common cause was overgrazing, but under-grazing was also an important factor. By 2004, the species was effectively extinct in Cumbria and had been reduced to only eight isolated colonies in Northern Ireland. In Wales, an assessment of habitat suggested that the butterfly would continue to decline unless substantial conservation action is undertaken.

On the positive side, ongoing surveys revealed many previously unknown colonies, especially in the Republic of Ireland, but also in Cornwall, Pembrokeshire and Snowdonia. Recent records from Lancashire and the Isle of Wight are believed to be releases. In its Scottish strongholds, the species recovered from low population levels in 2002. It remains under-recorded here and a number of new colonies were discovered recently. However, traditional low-intensity agriculture has an uncertain future, and either abandonment or intensification could spell disaster for the butterfly in Scotland. In Ireland, many colonies are threatened by land-use change, but increased awareness resulted in the recent translocation of one colony, which was in the path of a new motorway in County Clare.

The butterfly is increasing in some areas thanks to conservation management, resulting in the positive 10-year population trend at monitored sites. Several major landscape-scale conservation projects were initiated during the current period (e.g. in Carmarthenshire, Devon and on Salisbury Plain). Much of this work is to reverse the effects of recent neglect and instigate sustainable habitat improvements to benefit Marsh Fritillary populations in the long-term.

References: Fowles and Smith 2006, Hobson *et al.* 2002

2000–04
- 1 sighting
- 2–9 seen
- 10+ seen (260 squares)
- 1995–99
- 1970–82

There has been a significant long-term decrease in the abundance of the Marsh Fritillary at monitored sites in Britain.

Glanville Fritillary
Melitaea cinxia

UK BIODIVERSITY ACTION PLAN STATUS
Candidate Priority Species

DISTRIBUTION TREND (1970–82 vs 1995–2004)
Britain: -17% ⬇

POPULATION TREND
Britain: insufficient data

There has been no substantial change in the status of the Glanville Fritillary. It remains restricted to coastal habitats (particularly landslips) on the Isle of Wight, Guernsey and Alderney, and a single coastal colony in Hampshire.

At the beginning of the 2000–04 period, many populations on the Isle of Wight appeared to be in decline and one isolated colony on the eastern side of the island was feared extinct. However, the latter proved not to be the case and, across the island, Glanville Fritillary numbers improved from 2002 onwards, ending the current period with good population levels.

The species appears stable on Guernsey and Alderney, but the Hampshire population seems to have declined in recent years. The butterfly has been released elsewhere but with the exception of the colony shown in Somerset, has failed to become established. This is hardly surprising since the releases are often undertaken at unsuitable sites without the knowledge or support of land managers.

Despite no major change in recent years, the Glanville Fritillary remains a very rare and vulnerable butterfly at the edge of its European range in England, and it is potentially threatened by engineering works to stabilise coastal habitats. Consequently, it has been put forward as a candidate for Priority Species status in the UK BAP.

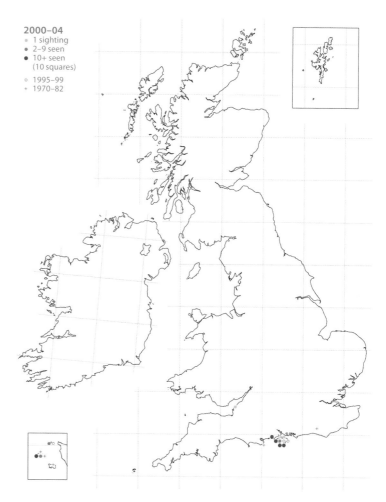

2000–04
- 1 sighting
- 2–9 seen
- 10+ seen
  (10 squares)
○ 1995–99
+ 1970–82

Heath Fritillary
Melitaea athalia

UK BIODIVERSITY ACTION PLAN STATUS
Priority Species

DISTRIBUTION TREND (1970–82 vs 1995–2004)
Britain: -25% ⬇

POPULATION TREND
Long-term (1984–2004)   10-year (1995–2004)
Britain: -73% ⬇   Britain: -46% ⬇

Considering the distribution and population trends for the Heath Fritillary, the continued survival of this rare species in Britain is, in itself, a notable conservation achievement.

As the population plot (which includes timed count data as well as transects) shows, the 2000–04 period was one of reduced numbers at monitored sites overall, with particularly low counts in 2000, 2001 and 2003 (respectively, the fourth, sixth and fifth lowest yet recorded). These contributed to a significant long-term decline (jointly with the Marsh Fritillary as the worst decline of any species), which had shown little sign of abating in recent years. However, by 2004, population levels had risen substantially and there was better news for the species. Carefully targeted habitat management (coppicing and ride widening) in the Blean Woods complex in Kent had restored the number of colonies to the 1980 level (25), meeting the UK BAP target for this area. Ongoing management is vital to maintain and extend this success.

On Exmoor, the butterfly's other main stronghold, 50% of colonies were lost between 1989 and 2000. Eight further colonies became extinct during the current period and the Heath Fritillary was lost from the western part of Exmoor. However, renewed habitat management efforts (burning and bracken control) have produced promising early results, including new colonisations and increased population counts.

Elsewhere, populations established by conservation organisations in Essex and Devon have continued to thrive, but one of the two remaining colonies in Cornwall became extinct during the 2000–04 period.

References: Brereton 2006, Bulman 2004, Holloway *et al.* 2003, McCracken *et al.* 2005, Wigglesworth *et al.* 2004

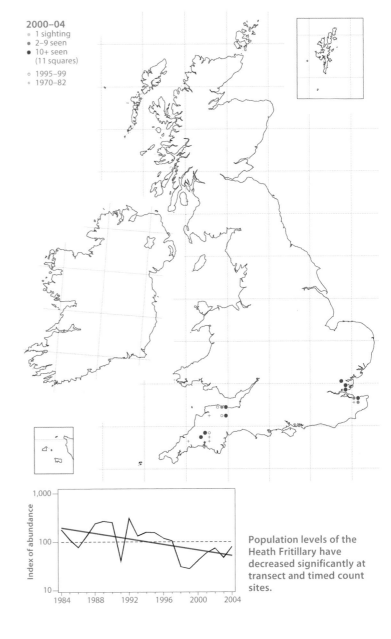

2000–04
- 1 sighting
- 2–9 seen
- 10+ seen
  (11 squares)
- 1995–99
+ 1970–82

Population levels of the Heath Fritillary have decreased significantly at transect and timed count sites.

Speckled Wood
Pararge aegeria

UK BIODIVERSITY ACTION PLAN STATUS
Not listed

DISTRIBUTION TREND (1970–82 vs 1995–2004)
Britain: +31% ⬆   Ireland: Stable ▪

POPULATION TREND
Long-term (1976–2004)   10-year (1995–2004)
Britain: +160% ⬆   Britain: +66% ⬆

The Speckled Wood continued a major range expansion (see map on p.79) and significant long-term increase in population level during the 2000–04 period. Its distribution in southern Britain continued to spread rapidly northwards and many new 10km squares were colonised, particularly in southern Yorkshire and along the east coast up into Northumberland.

Considerable gains were made in Scotland too, both on the west coast and in the east around the Moray Firth. These two formerly isolated populations seem destined to become connected in the near future, if they are not already. Perhaps most significantly, the Speckled Wood was recorded in several places in the forests of Perth and Kinross, presumably having moved southwards over the Grampian Mountains. The butterfly was also recorded for the first time in the Western Isles, in one of the few wooded areas on Lewis, and is maintaining good numbers there.

The population level of the Speckled Wood was very high at monitored sites in each year of the 2000–04 period with the exception of 2001 (although counts were still above the long-term average that year). Numbers in 2003 were the second highest since monitoring began in 1976, and 2004 provided the fourth highest level recorded.

In addition to high population levels, there were some extraordinarily early Speckled Wood sightings in 2004. The first was on 4th February, but it was quickly followed by several others across southern counties of England. In recent years, first sightings have typically been in early or mid-March, with widespread emergence in April.

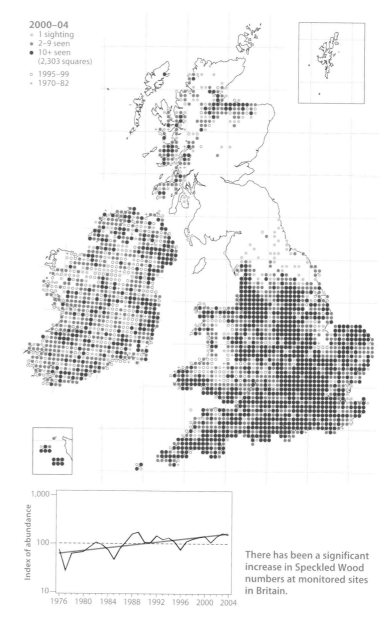

2000–04
· 1 sighting
● 2–9 seen
● 10+ seen
(2,303 squares)
○ 1995–99
+ 1970–82

There has been a significant increase in Speckled Wood numbers at monitored sites in Britain.

Wall
Lasiommata megera

UK BIODIVERSITY ACTION PLAN STATUS
Candidate Priority Species

DISTRIBUTION TREND (1970–82 vs 1995–2004)
Britain: -38% ⬇   Ireland:
Medium decrease ⬇

POPULATION TREND
Long-term (1976–2004)   10-year (1995–2004)
Britain: -65% ⬇   Britain: -2% ⬇

The decline of inland populations of the Wall since the 1970s has been dramatic and severe. The decrease in distribution of this once widespread and common butterfly meets the criteria for Priority Species status in the UK BAP; something that would have been unimaginable to entomologists 25 years ago. In addition, population levels at monitored sites have declined significantly over the long term.

There was little evidence of improvement in the status of the Wall during the 2000–04 period. Population levels remained well below the long-term average in each year (although the trend is no longer one of rapid decline) and the distribution map suggests continuing losses in southern and midland England.

In contrast, the Wall seems to be colonising new sites at the northern edge of its range, particularly in Northumberland and Yorkshire. In addition, the species has been rediscovered on the west coast of Scotland (on Mull), where there were no records at all in the 1995–99 period, but where the species was known from isolated sites in the 1970s.

In Ireland, it remains reasonably common around the coast. Improved surveying in west County Clare and north County Donegal yielded a substantial number of new 10km square records. There was even a glimmer of optimism from southern England, with Wall records from several 10km squares where the species was not found in the 1995–99 survey.

Research is underway to improve our understanding of this butterfly's ecology and the reasons for its demise in the south in recent decades.

Reference: Aldwell 2003

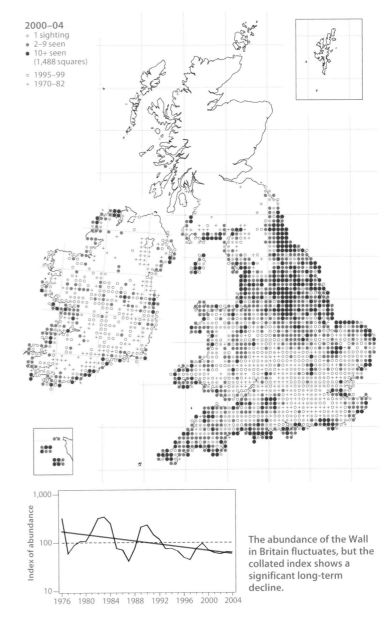

2000–04
- 1 sighting
- 2–9 seen
- 10+ seen
  (1,488 squares)
- 1995–99
- 1970–82

The abundance of the Wall in Britain fluctuates, but the collated index shows a significant long-term decline.

Mountain Ringlet
Erebia epiphron

UK BIODIVERSITY ACTION PLAN STATUS
Candidate Priority Species

DISTRIBUTION TREND (1970–82 vs 1995–2004)
Britain: -12% ⬇

POPULATION TREND
Britain: insufficient data

The Mountain Ringlet is the only truly montane butterfly in Britain and Ireland. Its high-altitude habitats and restricted periods of weather suitable for flight present considerable challenges to recording and monitoring. As a consequence, the status of the species remains poorly known relative to other butterflies.

The limited data available for the 2000–04 period provide little evidence of a significant change in distribution or population level. The butterfly was recorded in eight new 10km squares during the current survey, but not reported from 16 squares where there were 1995–99 records – a typical pattern for an under-recorded species.

Two 10km squares within the Scottish range of the Mountain Ringlet have no butterfly records at all (recent or historic) in the BNM database while many others have been visited only rarely by butterfly recorders. Further recording effort is needed and hill walkers, who have provided some important recent records, are encouraged to help improve our knowledge of this butterfly.

However, specific surveys in 2004 suggested that the Mountain Ringlet had been lost at many previously occupied sites, particularly at lower altitudes. These losses, together with the severe threat posed by climate change, led to the species being put forward as a candidate UK BAP Priority Species.

References: Franco *et al.* in press, Hill *et al.* 2002

2000–04
- 1 sighting
- 2–9 seen
- 10+ seen
  (31 squares)
- 1995–99
+ 1970–82

Scotch Argus
Erebia aethiops

UK BIODIVERSITY ACTION PLAN STATUS
Not listed

DISTRIBUTION TREND (1970–82 vs 1995–2004)
Britain: -10% ⬇

POPULATION TREND
Long-term (1979–2004)   10-year (1995–2004)
Britain: +165% ⬆   Britain: -1% ⬇

Recording in the 2000–04 period located Scotch Argus colonies in 87 new 10km squares in Scotland. It is assumed that this is due to previous under-recording. Notable records came from Kintyre and Islay on the west coast and from the north-east of Highland, areas with no 1995–99 records and very few historical ones.

New colonies were also located at the southern edge of the butterfly's range in Borders and Dumfries and Galloway, and the species has fared well at its two remaining sites in Cumbria.

Population monitoring during the current period showed that 2002 and 2003 were particularly good years.

Although there is some evidence of long-term distribution decline and a predicted threat from climate change, populations at monitored sites have increased significantly and the Scotch Argus is not currently considered a conservation priority in Britain.

Ecological research during the 2000–04 period revealed that Scotch Argus larvae feed on a wide range of grasses (as in continental Europe) rather than relying mainly on Purple Moor-grass (*Molinia caerulea*) as had been thought previously. In Scotland, larvae were found feeding on Tufted Hair-grass (*Deschampsia cespitosa*), Wavy Hair-grass (*D. flexuosa*), Sheep's-fescue (*Festuca ovina*), Common Bent (*Agrostis capillaris*) and Sweet Vernal-grass (*Anthoxanthum odoratum*).

Reference: Kirkland 2005

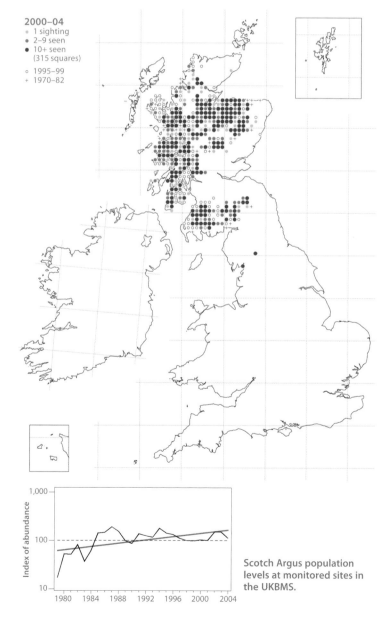

2000–04
- 1 sighting
- 2–9 seen
- 10+ seen (315 squares)
○ 1995–99
+ 1970–82

Scotch Argus population levels at monitored sites in the UKBMS.

Marbled White
Melanargia galathea

UK BIODIVERSITY ACTION PLAN STATUS
Not listed

DISTRIBUTION TREND (1970–82 vs 1995–2004)
Britain: +11% ⬆

POPULATION TREND
Long-term (1976–2004)   10-year (1995–2004)
Britain: +129% ⬆   Britain: -15% ⬇

The Marbled White continued to extend its distribution during the 2000–04 period and populations levels remained above the long-term average in each year except 2002. However, counts at monitored sites were lower than the high levels recorded in the late 1990s, which suggests that the rate of distribution increase may have slowed in recent years.

Interpretation of the changing distribution of the Marbled White is made difficult by releases. Many of the records in the East Midlands and southern Yorkshire are believed to be releases, as are those recorded in south Cumbria in the current period. The records in Durham relate to a population founded as part of university research into the effects of climate change, whist the origin of individuals seen in Cheshire and Norfolk is unknown.

Despite the unhelpful confusion caused by unauthorised releases, the number of new 10km squares recorded around the butterfly's core range in southern England and Wales provides strong evidence of continued, natural colonisation.

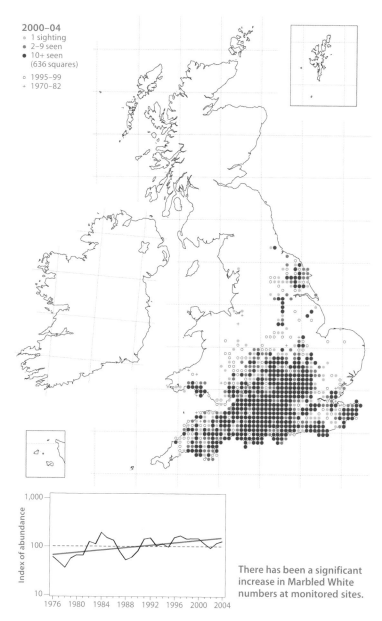

2000–04
- 1 sighting
- 2–9 seen
- 10+ seen
 (636 squares)
○ 1995–99
+ 1970–82

There has been a significant increase in Marbled White numbers at monitored sites.

Grayling
Hipparchia semele

UK BIODIVERSITY ACTION PLAN STATUS
Candidate Priority Species

DISTRIBUTION TREND (1970–82 vs 1995–2004)
Britain: -45% ⬇   Ireland:
                         Medium decrease ⬇

POPULATION TREND
Long-term (1976–2004)   10-year (1995–2004)
Britain: -51% ⬇   Britain: -41% ⬇

The Grayling is in serious decline. Long-term trends since the 1970s reveal this clearly and the species has been put forward for UK BAP Priority Species status as a result.

In the 2000–04 period, distribution recording led to the discovery of many new colonies, particularly on the west coasts of Scotland and Ireland, whilst population monitoring showed the ongoing decline of the Grayling. Populations at monitored sites declined from being about average in 2000, to the second worst level yet recorded in 2002. Although still very poor by comparison to the long-term average, numbers did improve slightly in 2003 and 2004. The 10-year trend shows a significant decline in population levels since the mid-1990s.

In England, the most notable records in the current survey came from Yorkshire and north-east England, where the species is very rare. Several new Grayling colonies were discovered here on brownfield sites, including a large population on extensive brownfield land along the River Tees in Middlesbrough. Measures have already been taken to conserve the butterfly at some of these sites.

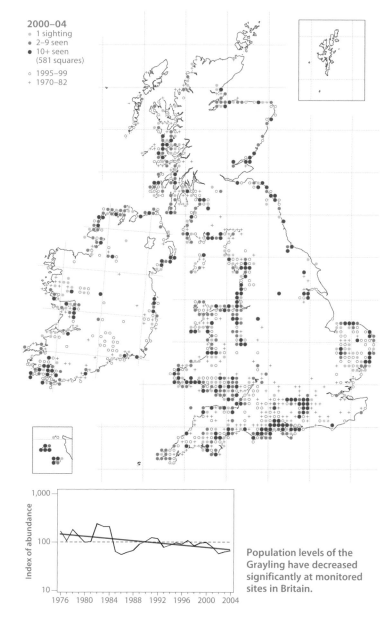

2000–04
- 1 sighting
- 2–9 seen
- 10+ seen
  (581 squares)
- 1995–99
+ 1970–82

Population levels of the Grayling have decreased significantly at monitored sites in Britain.

Gatekeeper
Pyronia tithonus

UK BIODIVERSITY ACTION PLAN STATUS
Not listed

DISTRIBUTION TREND (1970–82 vs 1995–2004)
Britain: +12% ⬆   Ireland:
                    Medium decrease ⬇

POPULATION TREND
Long-term (1976–2004)   10-year (1995–2004)
Britain: -12% ⬇   Britain: -5% ⬇

The Gatekeeper continued to expand its distribution in Britain during 2000–04, particularly in northern Yorkshire and County Durham, and in the Pennines (see map on p.79).

In Ireland the situation is less clear, probably because of low levels of recording in both recent and historical periods. The long-term distribution trend indicates a decline, but the butterfly was recorded in new 10km squares during 2000–04, particularly in County Cork. All of these changes are within its historical range and there is little sign yet in Ireland of the northwards expansion that is expected with climate change. This may be due to a 'barrier' of high ground to the north of the Gatekeeper's current range.

British population levels of the Gatekeeper improved towards the end of the current period after a succession of average or below average years. Counts at monitored sites in 2004 were well above the long-term average and the highest since 1996.

Within its range, this remains a very common and widespread butterfly, with no current threats evident at this time.

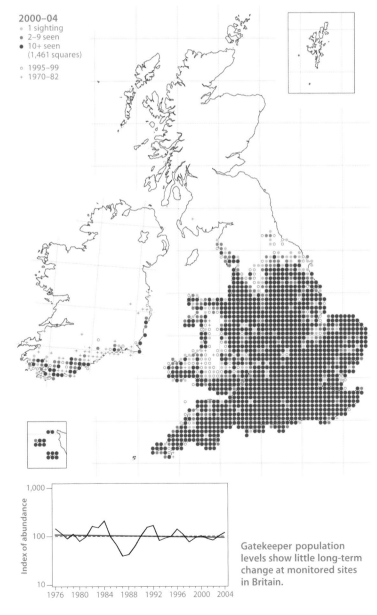

2000–04
- 1 sighting
- 2–9 seen
- 10+ seen
  (1,461 squares)
○ 1995–99
+ 1970–82

Gatekeeper population levels show little long-term change at monitored sites in Britain.

UK BIODIVERSITY ACTION PLAN STATUS
Not listed

DISTRIBUTION TREND (1970–82 vs 1995–2004)
Britain: -4% ⬇   Ireland:
                        Small decrease ⬇

POPULATION TREND
Long-term (1976–2004)   10-year (1995–2004)
Britain: +28% ⬆   Britain: -5% ⬇

The status of the Meadow Brown showed no major change during the 2000–04 period. It remains the most abundant butterfly in Britain (more Meadow Browns are recorded on butterfly transects than any other species) and the second most widespread species in Britain and Ireland (after the Green-veined White).

The Meadow Brown was under-recorded in the Republic of Ireland during the previous survey (1995–99) and was found in over 200 new 10km squares as a result of continued recording in 2000–04.

Long-term population monitoring of the Meadow Brown in Britain indicates a small increase, but there was little deviation from average levels during the 2000–04 period; 2000 and 2003 were relatively good years (although not as good as 1998 or 1999) and 2001 and 2002 were slightly below average.

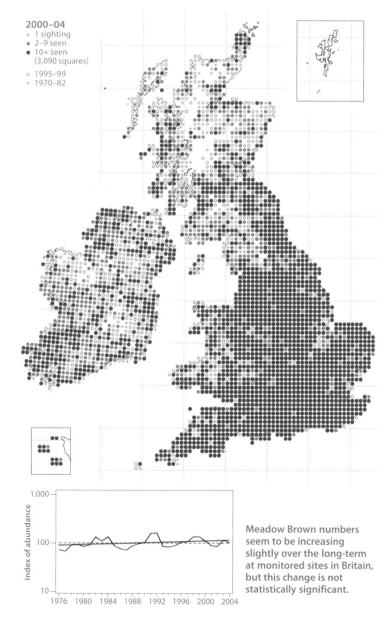

2000–04
· 1 sighting
• 2–9 seen
● 10+ seen
   (3,090 squares)
○ 1995–99
+ 1970–82

Meadow Brown numbers seem to be increasing slightly over the long-term at monitored sites in Britain, but this change is not statistically significant.

Ringlet
Aphantopus hyperantus

UK BIODIVERSITY ACTION PLAN STATUS
Not listed

DISTRIBUTION TREND (1970–82 vs 1995–2004)
Britain: +16% ⬆   Ireland: Stable ▪

POPULATION TREND
Long-term (1976–2004)   10-year (1995–2004)
Britain: +373% ⬆   Britain: +33% ⬆

The Ringlet continued to do well across Britain and Ireland in the 2000–04 period. The significant increase in population level since the 1970s continued, with counts well above the long-term average at monitored sites in Britain in each year of the current period. Indeed, the population levels in 2003 and 2000 were the highest and second highest (respectively) since monitoring began in 1976.

Not surprisingly, the Ringlet also expanded its distribution by colonising new areas during the most recent five-year period (see map on p.79). New 10km squares were recorded at its range margin in north-west England, in Northumberland and in Scotland. Most dramatic was a significant movement into Highland, particularly during 2004, which brought records from both southern and northern ends of the Great Glen and from several locations along the River Spey in the western Cairngorms.

In Ireland, the Ringlet was recorded in 279 new 10km squares in the 2000–04 survey, half as many again as the total number reported in 1995–99. This is thought to be due to increased recording effort. However, the butterfly does seem to be becoming progressively scarcer in areas with intensive agriculture.

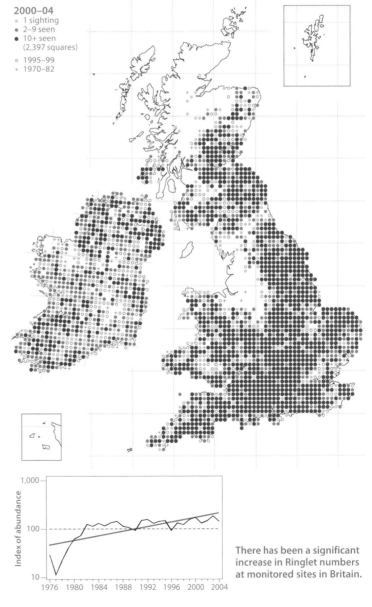

2000–04
- 1 sighting
- 2–9 seen
- 10+ seen (2,397 squares)
- 1995–99
+ 1970–82

There has been a significant increase in Ringlet numbers at monitored sites in Britain.

Small Heath
Coenonympha pamphilus

UK BIODIVERSITY ACTION PLAN STATUS
Candidate Priority Species

DISTRIBUTION TREND (1970–82 vs 1995–2004)
Britain: -29% ⬇   Ireland:
                     Medium decrease ⬇

POPULATION TREND
Long-term (1976–2004)   10-year (1995–2004)
Britain: -52% ✳⬇   Britain: -29% ⬇

The 2000–04 period brought much-needed good news for the beleaguered Small Heath. Population levels had decreased in each year since 1997, and in 2000 and 2002 they reached their lowest points since monitoring began in 1976. However, 2003 was a much better year for the Small Heath and counts soared to just above the long-term average. Populations decreased slightly in 2004, and it remains to be seen whether this recovery can be sustained.

Despite this recent upturn in the Small Heath's fortunes, the long-term population trend is a significant and severe decrease, and the butterfly now meets the criteria for Priority Species status in the UK BAP. The long-term distribution trend also gives cause for concern.

In the Republic of Ireland, intensive survey work in County Donegal has led to a massive increase in the recorded distribution of the Small Heath. Although this suggests that the butterfly remains under-recorded in the country as a whole, the species seems to have become very scarce in intensively farmed areas in the south, east and midlands of Ireland.

The ecological requirements of the Small Heath are insufficiently understood, and further research is needed to help reverse its decline.

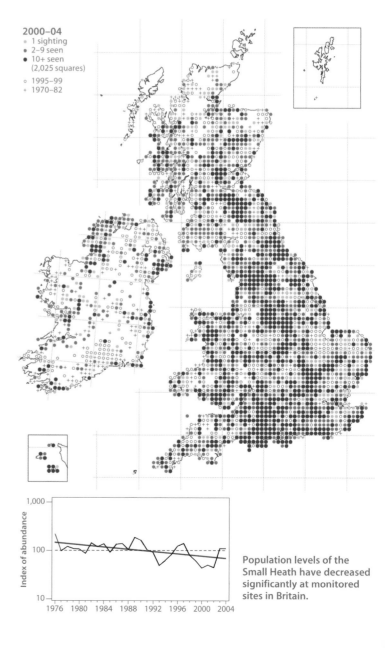

2000–04
- 1 sighting
- 2–9 seen
- 10+ seen
  (2,025 squares)
- 1995–99
+ 1970–82

Population levels of the Small Heath have decreased significantly at monitored sites in Britain.

Large Heath
Coenonympha tullia

UK BIODIVERSITY ACTION PLAN STATUS
Candidate Priority Species

DISTRIBUTION TREND (1970–82 vs 1995–2004)
Britain: -43% ⬇   Ireland:
                       Medium decrease ⬇

POPULATION TREND
Long-term (1978–2004)   10-year (1995–2004)
Britain: -26% ⬇   Britain: +58% ⬆

Although the Large Heath merits Priority Species status in the UK BAP because of its long-term distribution decline, recording during the 2000–04 period suggested that recent losses may not be quite as severe as feared.

The butterfly was rediscovered in many 10km squares with historical (but not 1995–99) records, for example in Dumfries and Galloway and in northern Highland, and more new squares were added in Ireland than were known in the 1995–99 period. Targeted surveys in Northumberland found little evidence of decline over the past decade and previously unknown colonies were discovered in the North York Moors.

Many of these finds coincided with high population levels at monitored sites in 2003 and 2004 (the highest levels since 1988). The 10-year population trend reflects this apparent upturn in the butterfly's fortunes, at least on monitored sites.

Nevertheless, there have been colony extinctions in recent years and, in some areas, many remaining sites are threatened by land-use change. In south-west Scotland for example, important colonies are at risk from landfill, drainage and golf course development. In Ireland, the increase in distribution is indicative of previous under-recording, but significant destruction of the butterfly's peat bog habitats has continued. In 2004, targeted surveys of previously occupied British sites revealed widespread habitat destruction and losses of Large Heath colonies in recent decades.

Insidious changes in climate and nutrient enrichment may pose an even greater threat to the long-term future of the Large Heath. Computer simulations suggest that climatic conditions may become unsuitable for the butterfly across most of its current range in Britain and Ireland by the end of this century.

References: Franco *et al.* in press, Hill *et al.* 2002

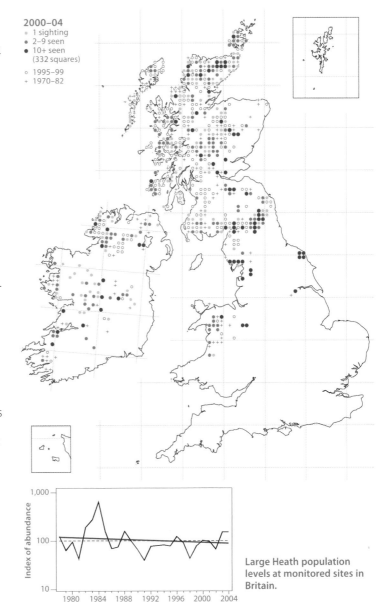

2000–04
- 1 sighting
- 2–9 seen
- 10+ seen
  (332 squares)
- 1995–99
- 1970–82

Large Heath population levels at monitored sites in Britain.

Rare migrants

There has been no obvious change in the status any of the rare migrant species during the 2000–04 period and these butterflies are not covered by individual species accounts in this book. Whilst the regular migrants (Clouded Yellow, Red Admiral and Painted Lady) have continued to provide much excitement for butterfly recorders (see species accounts), there have been few notable events involving the rarer species.

Perhaps the biggest disappointment was a run of poor years for sightings of the **Monarch** (*Danaus plexippus*) in Britain and Ireland, after the 1995–99 period had provided the two best years ever recorded (1995 and 1999). Only 2001 yielded a reasonable scatter of Monarch records, with sightings along the length of the south coast, from the Isles of Scilly to Kent, in October and early November. The number of sightings in 2001 was over 10 times that reported in any other year of the 2000–04 period[1], but less than a fifth of the 1999 total[2].

There was no evidence of breeding by the Queen of Spain Fritillary in Britain and Ireland during the 2000–04 period, extinguishing hopes that the butterfly had established a foothold here during 1995–99.

The **Camberwell Beauty** (*Nymphalis antiopa*), which last appeared in good numbers in 1995, also had just one significant immigration event during the 2000–04 period. This came in August 2002, when butterflies were reported from Cornwall to Shetland, with most sightings concentrated in east coast counties as is typical for this species. At least one Camberwell Beauty was reported from Suffolk, Norfolk, Lincolnshire, Yorkshire and Northumberland that month, but the total number of sightings was small compared with 1995.

Immigrant **Swallowtails** continued to be reported during the current survey, with several instances of more than one adult seen at a time and a few breeding records (see p.25). More unusually, there were breeding records of the **Long-tailed Blue** (*Lampides boeticus*) in Surrey in August and September 2003. However, there is no convincing evidence that these breeding attempts by the Long-tailed Blue and Swallowtail led to the establishment of resident populations. Similarly, there was no repeat of the regular sightings of the **Queen of Spain Fritillary** (*Issoria lathonia*) in 1995–97 in Suffolk (which may have represented a short-lived breeding colony), and no sightings at all from Jersey (where recorders had witnessed a steady increase in numbers up to 1999). Nevertheless, solitary immigrant individuals of this butterfly were reported occasionally from southern counties of England during the 2000–04 survey.

All of the other 'normal' rare migrants and vagrants were reported on at least one occasion during the 2000–04 period, although often such records are difficult to verify. These included **Scarce Swallowtail** (*Iphiclides podalirius*), **Pale Clouded Yellow** (*Colias hyale*), **Berger's Clouded Yellow** (*Colias alfacariensis*), **Black-veined White** (*Aporia crataegi*), **Bath White** (*Pontia daplidice*), **Short-tailed Blue** (*Cupido argiades*), **American Painted Lady** (*Vanessa virginiensis*) and **Large Tortoiseshell** (*Nymphalis polychloros*). Other species were reported occasionally, but these were attributed to illegal releases, accidental escapes from captive stock or, in the case of **Geranium Bronze** (*Cacyreus marshalli*) accidental importation with cultivated plants.

1   Assessment based on records reported to www.migrantmoth.com

2   Fox *et al.* 2001a

Chapter 4 **Results**

The collation and analysis of distribution records and monitoring data, through the Butterflies for the New Millennium (BNM) and UK Butterfly Monitoring Scheme (UKBMS) respectively, present a picture of continuing rapid change for Britain and Ireland's butterflies. This chapter summarises the main results from these data sets across different geographical areas: firstly for the whole of Britain and Ireland; secondly for Britain and Ireland separately; and finally for the devolved countries within Britain (England, Scotland and Wales).

Distribution of butterflies in Britain and Ireland

The number of species recorded in each 10km square is related not only to how many actually occur there, but also to the effectiveness of recording in revealing their presence. In some squares, particularly in areas with low human population density, the number of species will be underestimated because of insufficient recording. At the other extreme, very intensive recording may overestimate the actual number of breeding species in a square, as vagrant or migrant individuals are more likely to be observed[1]. Despite the possibility of these factors affecting some areas, the 2000–04 BNM survey achieved generally good coverage of Britain, Ireland, the Isle of Man, and the Channel Islands (see Chapter 2 for details) and as a result, the recorded distribution of species is considered to be a reasonable estimate of the actual species' richness.

More butterfly species (as well as more butterfly recorders) occur in southern parts of Britain, than in the north or in Ireland. This general pattern relates to the latitudinal gradient in climate, with southern areas experiencing warmer temperatures than those further north. Within this overall pattern, landscapes rich in good butterfly habitats can be seen clearly from the BNM results (map right), both in southern England (e.g. Salisbury Plain, the Isle of Purbeck in south Dorset, the North Downs and South Downs) and elsewhere (e.g. the Morecambe Bay Limestones in north-west England, the Gower in south Wales, the Burren in western Ireland and the coastline of County Down).

The number of 10km squares recorded for each species in the different survey periods across the whole BNM area is given in the Appendix. Results for Britain and Ireland separately, and for countries within Britain are shown in the tables later in this chapter. As explained in Chapter 2, the raw data have to be interpreted with care owing to the vastly different levels of recording effort in different periods. Thus, although the number of recorded squares for most species increased between the 1970–82 and 1995–2004 periods, much of this is due to the discovery of previously unknown colonies through more intensive recording. A sub-sampling method was therefore developed to overcome the biases resulting from different levels of recording effort in each period (see Chapter 2).

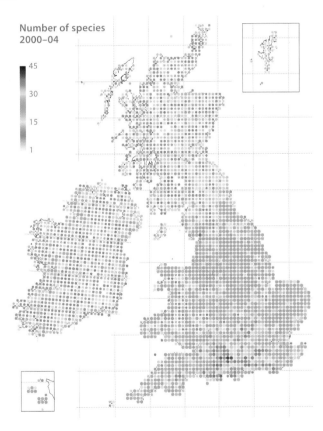

Number of species 2000–04

45
30
15
1

The number of species recorded in each 10km square in the 2000–04 survey period.

1 Dennis 2001

Expanding species

Despite the problems involved in interpreting change between different survey periods, the progressive and substantial range increases of some butterflies can be seen clearly since 1970–82. The maps for 15 such species are shown here. In most cases, it is obvious that the range expansion has occurred in a northerly/north-westerly direction, a pattern consistent with the predicted responses to climate change (see Chapter 5)[2].

The largest proportional increases in range have been those of the Essex Skipper, Comma, Holly Blue and Speckled Wood. Moreover, the distributions of a few species are now expanding after severe declines during the twentieth century (e.g. the Silver-spotted Skipper and Silver-washed Fritillary).

2 Hill *et al.* 2002

The maps on these pages show the expansions in range recorded for 15 species; they show the original distributions recorded in 1970–82, and additional 10km squares newly occupied in 1995–99 and in 2000–04.

Key
- 2000–04
- 1995–99
- 1970–82

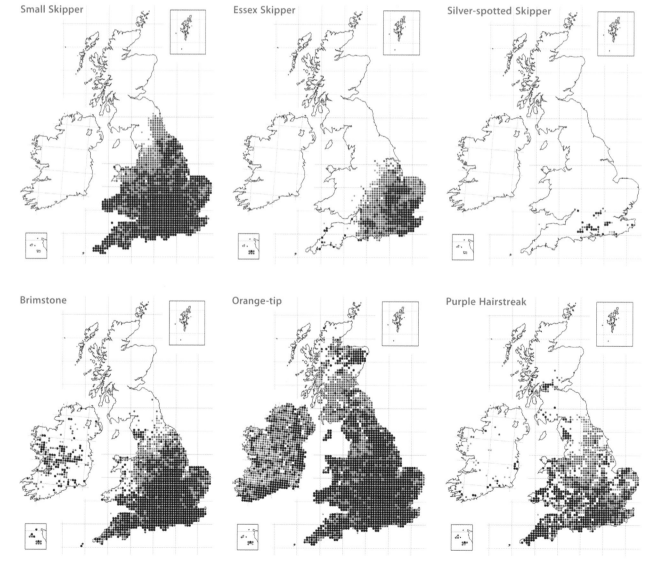

Small Skipper

Essex Skipper

Silver-spotted Skipper

Brimstone

Orange-tip

Purple Hairstreak

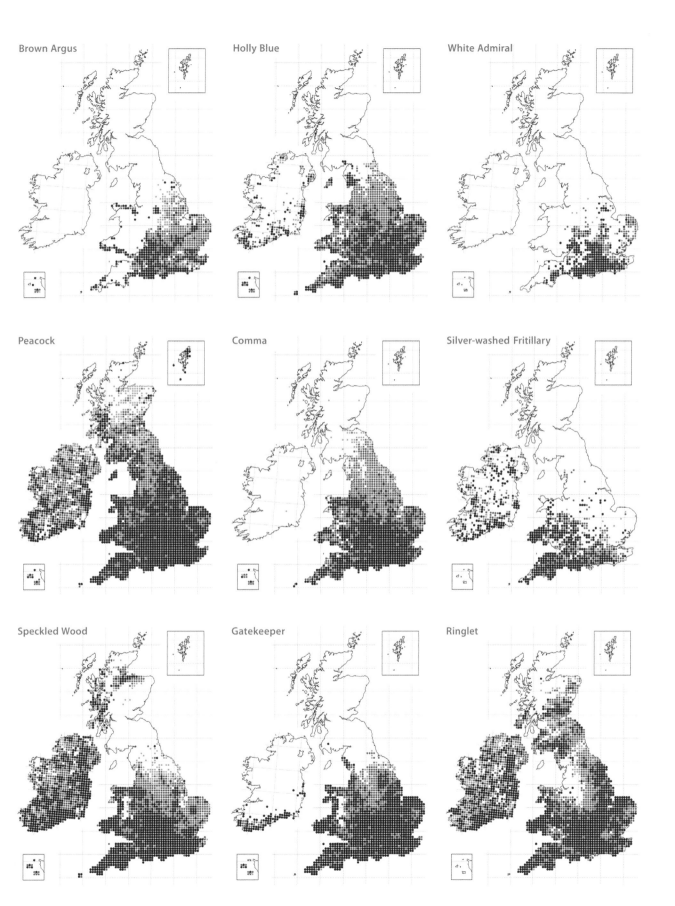

Brown Argus

Holly Blue

White Admiral

Peacock

Comma

Silver-washed Fritillary

Speckled Wood

Gatekeeper

Ringlet

Trends of butterflies in Britain

Both distribution records and population monitoring data were sufficiently comprehensive to enable a quantitative assessment of trends for butterflies that breed regularly in Britain (see Chapter 2 for analysis methods). Trends are presented in the table opposite and annual rates of population change are given in the Appendix.

The results show that the majority of species have declined since the 1970s, confirming the serious loss of butterflies reported in *The Millennium Atlas*[3]. The recorded distributions of 72% of the 57 butterfly species assessed have declined (when variation in recording effort is taken into account by sub-sampling). In contrast, the distributions of 28% of species have increased. If the three migrant species are excluded from the calculation, then 76% of species have declined and 24% increased. These results closely match the findings of previous studies using BNM data for 1995–99 only and an earlier version of the sub-sampling method[4].

Population trends from monitored sites show a slightly different pattern. Long-term trends show that 54% of assessed species have decreased in abundance while 46% have increased. Of these changes, around a third of the declines and increases are statistically significant (P<0.05), giving greater confidence in the interpretation of those trends. For most species, analyses of change in abundance and distribution present a very similar picture: overall there is a good correlation between assessments from the two sources of data. Species in decline tend to have negative distribution and population trends, whilst those that are doing well typically show increasing distributions and population levels.

A few species do not follow the general pattern and exhibit a substantial difference between distribution and population trends. There are several possible explanations for this phenomenon. Firstly, a species may appear to be faring better by one measure than the other, simply as an artefact of the different sampling methods (including the spatial scale of the assessment). Secondly, species may be faring better overall at sites where population monitoring is carried out because these are often protected areas of semi-natural habitat that are managed with biodiversity conservation in mind. Such species may be faring less well in the wider countryside, which is sampled better by the distribution survey. Finally, there is a greater time lag involved in the assessment of distribution change compared with population trends. Butterfly populations respond rapidly to changing environmental conditions (e.g. habitat quality or the weather) via direct effects on breeding success, but distributions are slower to respond, as changes are revealed only through the processes of colonisation and extinction.

The Adonis Blue, for example, has a distribution trend of -19% and a population trend of +28% since the 1970s. Our interpretation of the changing status of the butterfly is that it had suffered a long-term decline but has fared better in recent years. The negative distribution trend reflects the fact that there are still areas of the former range of the species that have not been recolonised, whilst the positive population trend shows that the species is recovering well at monitored sites.

Many of the species highlighted in these results as showing the greatest decreases or increases were also identified in previous assessments[5]. The most rapidly declining species include the High Brown Fritillary, Marsh Fritillary, Pearl-bordered Fritillary, Wood White, Duke of Burgundy, Grayling and Dingy and Grizzled Skippers. The species faring especially well include the Essex Skipper, Comma, Speckled Wood, Ringlet and Peacock. However, the inclusion, for the first time, of long-term population trends for almost all species has enabled the identification of other butterflies undergoing dramatic changes in their status. These include the Heath Fritillary, Small Pearl-bordered Fritillary, White Admiral and Small Heath, which are all in decline, and the Silver-spotted Skipper and Adonis Blue, which are recovering after suffering severe declines in previous decades. This emphasises the value of both data sources to inform conservation policy.

3 Asher *et al.* 2001
4 J.A. Thomas *et al.* 2004, Warren *et al.* 2001a
5 Asher *et al.* 2001, Warren *et al.* 1997

Analysis of the species records, distribution trends and population trends across Britain. Recorded distributions and distribution trends relate to Britain and the Isle of Man, population trends are for Britain only. Statistically significant population trends are marked as follows: * P<0.05, ** P<0.01, *** P<0.001; '–' indicates insufficient data to assess a trend.

	Recorded distribution (10km squares)				Distribution trend 1970–82 vs 1995–2004 ±standard deviation from sub-sampling	Population trends and significance level	
	1970–1982	1995–2004	'Lost'	'Gained'		Long-term[#]	10-year (1995–2004)
Chequered Skipper	34	32	11	9	-38% ± 0.8%	–	–
Small Skipper	1,098	1,549	21	472	4% ± 0.2%	–	–
Essex Skipper	302	717	15	430	46% ± 0.4%	–	–
Lulworth Skipper	13	13	2	2	-15% ± 0.9%	-13%	79%
Silver-spotted Skipper	25	43	7	25	4% ± 1.2%	1,524% ***	2%
Large Skipper	1,245	1,642	51	448	-12% ± 0.2%	12%	-38% *
Dingy Skipper	627	657	219	249	-48% ± 0.2%	-37% **	-26%
Grizzled Skipper	419	426	139	146	-49% ± 0.3%	-34%	-42%
Swallowtail	13	80	6	73	-5% ± 3.0%	–	–
Wood White	126	97	75	46	-65% ± 0.4%	-64%	10%
Clouded Yellow	269	1,486	16	1,233	144% ± 0.8%	1,117%	1,877%
Brimstone	942	1,362	28	448	-3% ± 0.2%	22%	-11%
Large White	1,926	2,321	94	489	-7% ± 0.1%	-28%	18%
Small White	1,857	2,185	95	423	-7% ± 0.1%	15%	-34%
Green-veined White	2,168	2,619	25	476	-1% ± 0.1%	11%	7%
Orange-tip	1,473	2,158	43	728	7% ± 0.1%	22%	-8%
Green Hairstreak	686	1,128	171	613	-29% ± 0.2%	-25%	-25%
Brown Hairstreak	170	155	57	42	-43% ± 0.4%	–	–
Purple Hairstreak	593	1,130	88	625	-15% ± 0.3%	53%	-23%
White-letter Hairstreak	470	750	155	435	-53% ± 0.3%	-71% *	-63%
Black Hairstreak	26	29	6	9	-43% ± 1.2%	–	–
Small Copper	1,659	2,137	78	556	-16% ± 0.1%	-8%	-41%
Small Blue	222	291	63	132	-38% ± 0.4%	-6%	121%
Silver-studded Blue	119	104	50	35	-43% ± 0.3%	-1%	-72% *
Brown Argus	376	842	41	507	16% ± 0.5%	16%	-61% *
Northern Brown Argus	68	158	10	100	18% ± 1.1%	-10%	-30%
Common Blue	1,886	2,421	104	639	-15% ± 0.1%	9%	-21%
Chalkhill Blue	205	226	46	67	-36% ± 0.3%	31%	-34%
Adonis Blue	88	113	22	47	-19% ± 0.6%	28%	63%
Holly Blue	813	1,521	17	725	36% ± 0.2%	281%	-30%
Duke of Burgundy	126	117	46	37	-52% ± 0.5%	-28%	-58% *
White Admiral	276	441	49	214	-31% ± 0.4%	-62% **	-36%
Purple Emperor	75	112	25	62	-52% ± 0.8%	-18%	33%
Red Admiral	1,544	2,506	30	992	25% ± 0.1%	350% ***	-38%
Painted Lady	1,288	2,453	34	1,199	32% ± 0.1%	520%	118%
Small Tortoiseshell	2,122	2,539	52	469	-3% ± 0.1%	-15%	-34%
Peacock	1,546	2,296	18	768	17% ± 0.1%	90% **	-40%
Comma	885	1,652	14	781	37% ± 0.2%	305% ***	64%
Small Pearl-bordered Fritillary	673	879	216	422	-34% ± 0.2%	-70% ***	-10%
Pearl-bordered Fritillary	381	288	219	126	-61% ± 0.2%	-66% **	-51%
High Brown Fritillary	127	57	97	27	-79% ± 0.3%	-13%	-85% *
Dark Green Fritillary	710	1,151	217	658	-30% ± 0.2%	63%	-10%
Silver-washed Fritillary	412	571	84	243	-29% ± 0.2%	33%	-14%
Marsh Fritillary	283	259	139	115	-46% ± 0.3%	-73% **	73%
Glanville Fritillary	8	10	2	4	-17% ± 1.8%	–	–
Heath Fritillary	17	14	5	2	-25% ± 0.9%	-73% **	-46%
Speckled Wood	985	1,680	21	716	31% ± 0.2%	160% ***	66% *
Wall	1,396	1,504	174	282	-38% ± 0.1%	-65% **	-2%
Mountain Ringlet	34	47	10	23	-12% ± 0.9%	–	–
Scotch Argus	244	414	29	199	-10% ± 0.6%	165% **	-1%
Marbled White	431	749	15	333	11% ± 0.3%	129% **	-15%
Grayling	596	676	192	272	-45% ± 0.2%	-51% **	-41% **
Gatekeeper	1,107	1,475	11	379	12% ± 0.1%	-12%	-5%
Meadow Brown	2,075	2,536	43	504	-4% ± 0.1%	28%	-5%
Ringlet	1,143	1,884	30	771	16% ± 0.2%	373% ***	33%
Small Heath	1,870	2,235	174	539	-29% ± 0.1%	-52% **	-29%
Large Heath	294	432	105	243	-43% ± 0.3%	-26%	58%

[#]The start date for the long-term population trend varies from species to species. See species accounts for details.

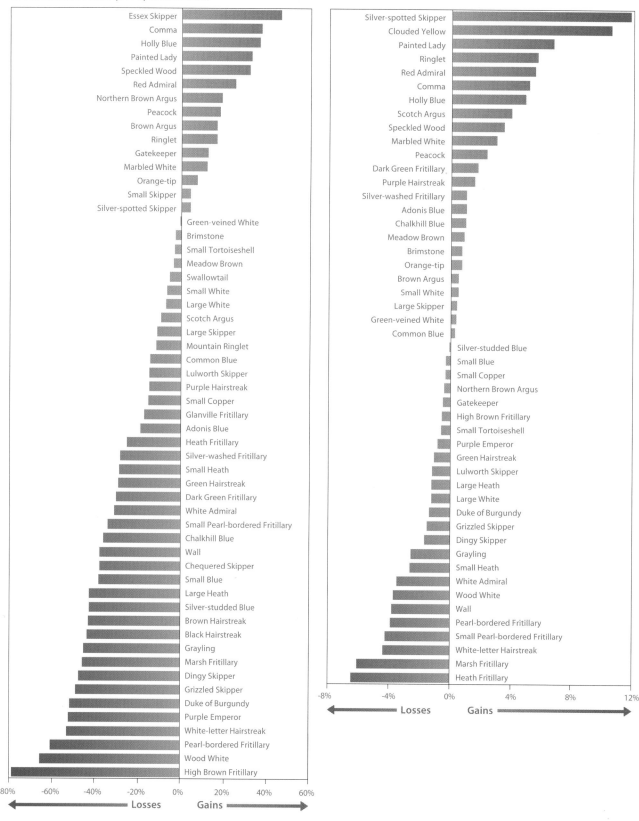

Percentage distribution trends for butterflies in Britain and the Isle of Man between 1970–82 and 1995–2004. The large increase of the Clouded Yellow (144%) is not shown.

Long-term population trends (shown as annual % change) for butterflies in Britain (see species accounts for date periods).

Left chart (Losses / Gains, -80% to 60%):

Essex Skipper
Comma
Holly Blue
Painted Lady
Speckled Wood
Red Admiral
Northern Brown Argus
Peacock
Brown Argus
Ringlet
Gatekeeper
Marbled White
Orange-tip
Small Skipper
Silver-spotted Skipper
Green-veined White
Brimstone
Small Tortoiseshell
Meadow Brown
Swallowtail
Small White
Large White
Scotch Argus
Large Skipper
Mountain Ringlet
Common Blue
Lulworth Skipper
Purple Hairstreak
Small Copper
Glanville Fritillary
Adonis Blue
Heath Fritillary
Silver-washed Fritillary
Small Heath
Green Hairstreak
Dark Green Fritillary
White Admiral
Small Pearl-bordered Fritillary
Chalkhill Blue
Wall
Chequered Skipper
Small Blue
Large Heath
Silver-studded Blue
Brown Hairstreak
Black Hairstreak
Grayling
Marsh Fritillary
Dingy Skipper
Grizzled Skipper
Duke of Burgundy
Purple Emperor
White-letter Hairstreak
Pearl-bordered Fritillary
Wood White
High Brown Fritillary

Right chart (Losses / Gains, -8% to 12%):

Silver-spotted Skipper
Clouded Yellow
Painted Lady
Ringlet
Red Admiral
Comma
Holly Blue
Scotch Argus
Speckled Wood
Marbled White
Peacock
Dark Green Fritillary
Purple Hairstreak
Silver-washed Fritillary
Adonis Blue
Chalkhill Blue
Meadow Brown
Brimstone
Orange-tip
Brown Argus
Small White
Large Skipper
Green-veined White
Common Blue
Silver-studded Blue
Small Blue
Small Copper
Northern Brown Argus
Gatekeeper
High Brown Fritillary
Small Tortoiseshell
Purple Emperor
Green Hairstreak
Lulworth Skipper
Large Heath
Large White
Duke of Burgundy
Grizzled Skipper
Dingy Skipper
Grayling
Small Heath
White Admiral
Wood White
Wall
Pearl-bordered Fritillary
Small Pearl-bordered Fritillary
White-letter Hairstreak
Marsh Fritillary
Heath Fritillary

Recent changes

In addition to distribution and population trends since the 1970s, which are the main focus of this book, change can be assessed over the shorter term. The 10-year population trends presented for 1995–2004 have to be interpreted carefully though, as they may be influenced unduly by the large fluctuations in annual abundance that are the norm for butterflies and other insects.

It is always prudent, therefore, to compare short-term trends with long-term trends or, at the least, with the long-term average population level. A comparison of annual rates of change (see the Appendix) over the recent 10-year period (1995–2004) compared to the full period of monitoring (since 1976 for most species) can highlight species of conservation concern. The rate of decline is accelerating for species such as the Duke of Burgundy and High Brown Fritillary, whose populations show modest losses over the last three decades (-1.3% and -0.5% per annum respectively) but have fared much worse over the last 10 years (-9.1% and -18.8% per annum). The 10-year trend for the Brown Argus also shows a large population decline (-61% over 10 years), set against long-term distribution and population increases. In this case, the 10-year trend need not be of major conservation concern (unless it continues!) as population levels are still at the long-term average. The decline is from relatively high abundance in the mid-1990s, rather than suggesting a decrease from 'normal' long-term levels.

Short-term distribution trends can also be calculated using sub-sampling analysis to compare the 1995–99 and 2000–04 BNM surveys. Such an analysis has been carried out but the results are not presented here. Overall, most species had only small percentage change trends between the two recent survey periods (54% of species' trends were between +10% and -10%, and 75% were between +15% and -15%). This is reassuring evidence that survey coverage and intensity were broadly comparable between the two periods. Most of the species that showed relatively large short-term changes were those that are thought to be declining so rapidly (e.g. High Brown Fritillary -55%, Pearl-bordered Fritillary -42%, Duke of Burgundy -28%) or increasing so rapidly (e.g. Silver-spotted Skipper +27%, Peacock +12%, Speckled Wood +11%) that genuine distribution change might be detected between the consecutive five-year periods.

Nevertheless, there is some evidence of lower recording effort for some species and some areas in the 2000–04 period, which might distort short-term trends. The experience of recorders and conservationists on the ground suggests that the distribution of the Chequered Skipper, for example, has not changed substantially since 1995, yet the short-term sub-sampling analysis yielded a trend of -26%, the fourth highest decline of any species. For these reasons, we have chosen to use the more comprehensive coverage obtained by combining all of the 1995–2004 BNM data in one survey as the most robust way of comparing distribution change with the historical baseline.

The addition of comparable new data sets from future BNM surveys, along with more detailed analysis, will open new opportunities to assess distribution change over shorter time periods.

Trends of butterflies in Ireland

Butterfly recording and monitoring are not as comprehensive across Ireland as a whole compared with Britain (although some parts of Ireland are better recorded than some parts of Britain). At present there are too few monitoring transects to enable the calculation of population trends that would be representative of species' change in Ireland. In addition, although great efforts have been made to record butterfly distributions in Ireland, coverage is limited, particularly in the earlier (1970–82) survey period. Although we used sub-sampling to assess distribution change for Ireland, the method was unable to correct satisfactorily for the large recording effort bias. Therefore, in agreement with the Dublin Naturalists' Field Club and the Northern Ireland Branch of Butterfly Conservation, we have presented a summary analysis of butterfly distribution change only. Whilst not yielding an exact percentage change

	Recorded distribution (10km squares)		
	1970–1982	1995–2004	Trend category
Dingy Skipper	35	95	Stable
Wood White/Réal's Wood White	209	343	Wood White: Insufficient data
			Réal's Wood White: Medium decrease
Clouded Yellow	85	338	Increase
Brimstone	83	182	Small decrease
Large White	471	723	Small decrease
Small White	460	662	Small decrease
Green-veined White	582	963	Stable
Orange-tip	364	898	Stable
Green Hairstreak	82	232	Small decrease
Brown Hairstreak	19	19	Small decrease
Purple Hairstreak	14	45	Stable
Small Copper	341	537	Medium decrease
Small Blue	42	85	Small decrease
Common Blue	386	589	Small decrease
Holly Blue	78	208	Increase
Red Admiral	298	723	Increase
Painted Lady	139	643	Increase
Small Tortoiseshell	541	817	Stable
Peacock	339	834	Increase
Comma	0	9	Vagrant
Pearl-bordered Fritillary	5	6	Insufficient data
Dark Green Fritillary	141	147	Medium decrease
Silver-washed Fritillary	179	289	Medium decrease
Marsh Fritillary	128	124	Severe decrease
Speckled Wood	516	901	Stable
Wall	306	407	Medium decrease
Grayling	127	205	Medium decrease
Gatekeeper	81	72	Medium decrease
Meadow Brown	615	916	Small decrease
Ringlet	442	844	Stable
Small Heath	243	405	Medium decrease
Large Heath	40	110	Medium decrease

Total numbers of 10km squares in which species were recorded in Ireland and the distribution trend assessed for 1970–2004 (see Chapter 3 p.15 for details).

figure for each species, this semi-quantitative approach is an improvement on previous assessments for Ireland[6] and is comparable to the approach adopted to gauge distribution trends across many other European countries[7].

The Marsh Fritillary was the only species considered to have undergone a severe decrease (50% or greater reduction in the number of occupied 10km squares), but nine species (31% of the resident butterflies) are believed to have suffered medium decreases (30–49% reduction) and a further eight (28% of species) small decreases (10–29% reduction). Thus, 62% of resident species have declined since the 1970s compared to only 7% that have increased (greater than 10% increase) and 24% that are stable (increases or decreases that were less than 10%). Other species were not assessed. If the three migrant breeding species (Clouded Yellow, Red Admiral and Painted Lady) are included, then the results become 56% of species declining, 16% species increasing and 22% stable. These overall proportions (i.e. including all regularly breeding species) are shown in the chart (right).

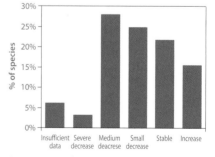

Percentage of regularly breeding species in each trend category in Ireland. More than half of the species are considered to have declined since the 1970s.

Distribution trends in England, Scotland and Wales

Distribution trends have been calculated for species in England, Scotland and Wales separately. As for the British trends, these country trends were derived from a sub-sampling analysis of the BNM data between 1970–82 and 1995–2004.

6 e.g. Asher et al. 2001
7 van Swaay and Warren 1999

Distribution trends for England, Scotland and Wales derived from sub-sampling. The recorded distribution is the count of 10km squares prior to sub-sampling.

	England Recorded distribution (10km squares)			Scotland Recorded distribution (10km squares)			Wales Recorded distribution (10km squares)		
	1970–1982	1995–2004	Trend	1970–1982	1995–2004	Trend	1970–1982	1995–2004	Trend
Chequered Skipper	9	1	-90% ± 0.5%	25	31	-19% ± 1.0%	–	–	–
Small Skipper	961	1,335	2% ± 0.2%	–	–	–	164	250	17% ± 0.4%
Essex Skipper	302	715	46% ± 0.4%	–	–	–	–	2	–
Lulworth Skipper	13	13	-15% ± 0.9%	–	–	–	–	–	–
Silver-spotted Skipper	25	43	4% ± 1.2%	–	–	–	–	–	–
Large Skipper	1,045	1,382	-12% ± 0.2%	32	61	-14% ± 1.2%	197	240	-11% ± 0.3%
Dingy Skipper	521	560	-46% ± 0.3%	27	21	-75% ± 1.0%	99	89	-49% ± 0.6%
Grizzled Skipper	393	411	-48% ± 0.3%	–	–	–	34	25	-62% ± 0.6%
Swallowtail	13	78	-8% ± 2.9%	–	1	–	–	1	–
Wood White	123	96	-65% ± 0.4%	–	–	–	8	8	-60% ± 2.0%
Clouded Yellow	223	1,166	138% ± 0.9%	11	157	244% ± 6.3%	36	188	164% ± 2.1%
Brimstone	878	1,238	-3% ± 0.2%	–	2	–	77	151	5% ± 0.8%
Large White	1,313	1,475	-2% ± 0.1%	415	604	-32% ± 0.4%	234	277	6% ± 0.3%
Small White	1,315	1,475	-2% ± 0.1%	343	471	-35% ± 0.3%	241	274	2% ± 0.3%
Green-veined White	1,338	1,475	-3% ± 0.1%	623	905	2% ± 0.2%	251	276	1% ± 0.2%
Orange-tip	1,151	1,436	-2% ± 0.1%	131	500	111% ± 0.8%	217	261	-1% ± 0.3%
Green Hairstreak	486	792	-27% ± 0.3%	123	235	-35% ± 0.7%	93	122	-38% ± 0.6%
Brown Hairstreak	127	125	-41% ± 0.4%	–	–	–	43	30	-50% ± 0.7%
Purple Hairstreak	491	993	-10% ± 0.4%	13	39	-10% ± 3.3%	100	126	-40% ± 0.7%
White-letter Hairstreak	421	715	-50% ± 0.4%	–	–	–	65	58	-68% ± 0.6%
Black Hairstreak	26	29	-43% ± 1.2%	–	–	–	–	–	–
Small Copper	1,186	1,434	-16% ± 0.1%	283	472	-24% ± 0.4%	225	267	-6% ± 0.3%
Small Blue	182	223	-43% ± 0.3%	23	35	-20% ± 1.7%	17	33	-9% ± 2.0%
Silver-studded Blue	108	93	-46% ± 0.4%	–	–	–	14	13	-21% ± 1.1%
Brown Argus	334	799	23% ± 0.5%	–	–	–	46	46	-43% ± 1.0%
Northern Brown Argus	13	31	12% ± 2.4%	55	128	20% ± 1.1%	–	–	–
Common Blue	1,189	1,436	-11% ± 0.1%	525	771	-27% ± 0.2%	204	248	-4% ± 0.3%
Chalkhill Blue	205	226	-36% ± 0.3%	–	–	–	–	–	–
Adonis Blue	88	113	-19% ± 0.6%	–	–	–	–	–	–
Holly Blue	720	1,316	35% ± 0.2%	4	3	–	105	226	46% ± 0.7%
Duke of Burgundy	126	117	-52% ± 0.5%	–	–	–	–	–	–
White Admiral	274	439	-31% ± 0.4%	–	–	–	6	5	-57% ± 2.2%
Purple Emperor	75	112	-52% ± 0.8%	–	–	–	–	–	–
Red Admiral	1,108	1,476	14% ± 0.1%	275	792	61% ± 0.6%	190	274	30% ± 0.4%
Painted Lady	937	1,470	23% ± 0.2%	200	743	74% ± 0.8%	172	274	31% ± 0.5%
Small Tortoiseshell	1,356	1,480	-1% ± 0.1%	552	820	-10% ± 0.3%	256	276	-2% ± 0.2%
Peacock	1,185	1,474	10% ± 0.1%	167	590	84% ± 0.8%	225	272	8% ± 0.2%
Comma	774	1,410	37% ± 0.2%	–	50	–	139	232	19% ± 0.6%
Small Pearl-bordered Fritillary	286	271	-54% ± 0.3%	235	453	-9% ± 0.5%	163	173	-36% ± 0.4%
Pearl-bordered Fritillary	227	151	-66% ± 0.2%	88	119	-33% ± 0.7%	76	23	-78% ± 0.2%
High Brown Fritillary	107	49	-78% ± 0.3%	–	–	–	23	11	-81% ± 0.7%
Dark Green Fritillary	356	551	-40% ± 0.3%	241	464	-15% ± 0.4%	114	152	-29% ± 0.6%
Silver-washed Fritillary	319	478	-23% ± 0.3%	–	–	–	105	110	-45% ± 0.7%
Marsh Fritillary	175	139	-58% ± 0.4%	31	45	-12% ± 1.2%	78	75	-32% ± 0.5%
Glanville Fritillary	8	10	-17% ± 1.8%	–	–	–	–	–	–
Heath Fritillary	17	14	-25% ± 0.9%	–	–	–	–	–	–
Speckled Wood	752	1,252	35% ± 0.2%	72	216	38% ± 1.0%	194	247	8% ± 0.3%
Wall	1,162	1,252	-41% ± 0.2%	47	40	-51% ± 0.8%	210	232	-18% ± 0.3%
Mountain Ringlet	6	7	-23% ± 2.1%	28	40	-9% ± 1.1%	–	–	–
Scotch Argus	2	2	0% ± 0.0%	242	412	-10% ± 0.6%	–	–	–
Marbled White	413	706	11% ± 0.3%	–	–	–	24	56	10% ± 1.5%
Grayling	330	345	-53% ± 0.3%	137	189	-42% ± 0.5%	136	150	-30% ± 0.5%
Gatekeeper	955	1,266	12% ± 0.2%	1	–	–	176	243	15% ± 0.3%
Meadow Brown	1,308	1,473	-2% ± 0.1%	554	822	-11% ± 0.3%	255	277	1% ± 0.2%
Ringlet	863	1,289	6% ± 0.2%	138	395	77% ± 0.7%	164	245	20% ± 0.5%
Small Heath	1,166	1,356	-30% ± 0.2%	514	662	-31% ± 0.2%	221	249	-17% ± 0.3%
Large Heath	40	59	-27% ± 1.3%	238	365	-44% ± 0.3%	22	17	-52% ± 1.0%

Distribution trends were broadly similar for England and Wales. The most obvious exceptions are species that have expanded their range in England but not in Wales. In most cases this is because the species are already found throughout Wales but not throughout England (for example, the Speckled Wood and Comma). The Brown Argus, on the other hand, has the potential to increase in both countries. Its core distribution has expanded rapidly from southern England towards isolated populations in other areas (e.g. Wales, the Midlands and south-west England). The trend in England is +23%. However, this expanding range margin has not yet reached Wales, where existing Brown Argus populations, which are typically restricted to semi-natural habitats, appear to have declined (the trend in Wales is -43%).

There are more substantial differences between trends for species in Scotland compared to those in England and Wales. With the exception of the Dingy Skipper, which seems to have fared particularly badly in Scotland (and has the greatest percentage distribution decline of any species in that country), most butterflies seem to have fared better than in England and Wales. The Pearl-bordered Fritillary, for example, has declined by 66% in England and 78% in Wales, but only by 33% in Scotland. Nevertheless, this is still a serious cause for concern. Similarly, the Small Pearl-bordered Fritillary, Dark Green Fritillary and Marsh Fritillary have all suffered much larger declines in England and Wales (particularly in England) than in Scotland.

Expanding species are prominent amongst the Scottish trends. Most of the distribution increase for butterflies such as the Orange-tip and Peacock has occurred in Scotland and is reflected in the percentage change figures. For example, across Britain as a whole, the Orange-tip has increased by only 7% and the Peacock by 17%, whereas in Scotland the changes are 111% and 84% respectively.

National trends provide vital information for prioritising conservation action within each country, as well as assessing the biodiversity and sustainable development initiatives of the devolved governments. With continued development of the UKBMS network of transects, it will be possible in future to assess country-level population trends to complement distribution analysis.

Interpreting trends: habitat specialists and wider countryside species

The interpretation of changes in species' status can be helped by dividing butterflies into ecological groups. Previous studies have divided butterflies into groups such as 'island' and 'matrix' species[8], 'habitat specialists' and 'wider countryside species'[9], sedentary and mobile species[10], and 'biotope specialist' and 'generalist' species[11]. Although there are some minor differences in the placement of species into each category, all these studies concluded that butterflies restricted to semi-natural habitats (which also tend to be sedentary species) had fared badly compared with other species over recent decades.

Another analysis tested for correlations between the changing status of species and the strategies of their larval foodplants (i.e. whether plants are competitors, stress-tolerators or ruderals[12]) and the biological and ecological attributes of butterflies[13]. This study confirmed previous findings that rare and rapidly declining butterflies tend to be those that occur in few habitats (biotopes), are single-brooded, have low mobility and use few larval foodplant species.

In *The Millennium Atlas of Butterflies in Britain and Ireland*[14], butterflies were assigned either as habitat specialists or wider countryside species primarily on the basis of whether their breeding habitats were limited to discrete fragments in the landscape (in lowland areas at least) or occurred widely through the farmed countryside and urban environment (see box). Habitat specialist butterflies breed in botanically-rich grassland, heathland, ancient woodland and bog, for example, whereas wider countryside species also breed along hedgerows, field margins and road verges, and in rough grassland, gardens, parks and secondary woodland.

8 Pollard and Eversham 1995, Pollard and Yates 1993
9 Asher *et al*. 2001, Warren *et al*. 2001a
10 Warren *et al*. 2001a
11 van Swaay *et al*. 2006
12 Grime *et al*. 1988
13 Dennis *et al*. 2004
14 Asher *et al*. 2001

Habitat specialists

Chequered Skipper	Large Blue
Lulworth Skipper	Duke of Burgundy
Silver-spotted Skipper	White Admiral
Dingy Skipper	Purple Emperor
Grizzled Skipper	Small Pearl-bordered Fritillary
Swallowtail	Pearl-bordered Fritillary
Wood White	High Brown Fritillary
Green Hairstreak	Dark Green Fritillary
Brown Hairstreak	Silver-washed Fritillary
Black Hairstreak	Marsh Fritillary
Small Blue	Glanville Fritillary
Silver-studded Blue	Heath Fritillary
Northern Brown Argus	Mountain Ringlet
Chalkhill Blue	Grayling
Adonis Blue	Large Heath

Wider countryside species

Small Skipper	Small Tortoiseshell
Essex Skipper	Peacock
Large Skipper	Comma
Réal's Wood White	Specled Wood
Brimstone	Wall
Large White	Scotch Argus
Small White	Marbled White
Green-veined White	Gatekeeper
Orange-tip	Meadow Brown
Purple Hairstreak	Ringlet
White-letter Hairstreak	Small Heath
Small Copper	
Brown Argus	
Common Blue	
Holly Blue	

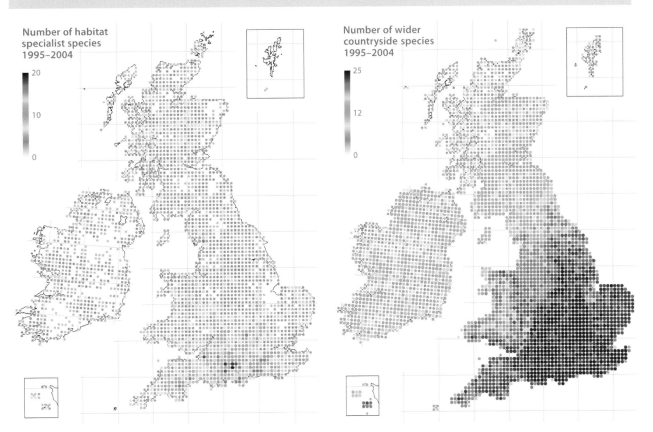

Number of habitat specialist species 1995–2004

Number of wider countryside species 1995–2004

It was recognised in *The Millennium Atlas* that the butterflies in each category tended to have similar ecological and life history characteristics, akin to specialists and generalists, but these were not used to classify the species. Thus, the Purple Hairstreak, which exhibits several features typical of a specialist species (for example, a high degree of larval foodplant specialisation, a single generation each year and not highly mobile), was classified as a wider countryside species because it breeds commonly in hedgerows, parks and gardens.

We used the same classification of habitat specialists and wider countryside species to compare the up-to-date distribution and population trends of each group. In the sub-sampling analysis of distribution change in Britain (1970–82 versus 1995–2004), 93% (27 of 29) of habitat specialists[15] had declined, compared

Maps showing the number of habitat specialist (left) and wider countryside species (right) recorded in each 10km square for the period 1995–2004. Note the different scale for each map. At this resolution, the distribution of wider countryside species seems unaffected by urban areas or intensive agriculture. The maps do not include 'wood whites' in Ireland.

15 Excludes the Large Blue

with 56% (14 of 25) of wider countryside species[16]. The Silver-spotted Skipper and the Northern Brown Argus were the only habitat specialist species that had positive distribution trends (and for the latter this is probably an artefact of improved recording). The mean distribution trends were -35% for habitat specialist species and +1% for wider countryside species.

Population monitoring data can also be used to assess the relative fortunes of habitat specialists and wider countryside species. Long-term population trends calculated from the UKBMS give a similar picture of change to that derived from distribution data, over approximately the same three-decade period. The long-term population trends of 78% (18/23) of habitat specialists had declined compared with 30% (7/23) of wider countryside species[17].

In addition to these proportional comparisons, UKBMS data for all habitat specialists and all wider countryside species can be combined into composite indices to assess how well populations of each group have done overall (see plot right). The composite index for habitat specialist butterflies reveals a significant 30% decrease over the 1976–2004 monitoring period, whilst the wider countryside species index shows a 27% increase. Thus, there are almost a third fewer habitat specialist butterflies in Britain now than in the mid-1970s, whereas the total abundance of wider countryside species has increased by over a quarter at monitored sites.

It is interesting that these two composite indices follow a very similar pattern over the last 10 years (1995–2004). The results show that the abundance of habitat specialists and wider countryside species have both decreased at monitored sites over that period (10-year trends of –20% and –19% respectively).

This analysis illustrates the potential of transect data to provide national and regional measures of the changing status of butterflies and, through these,

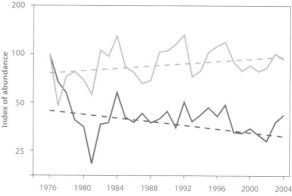

Composite collated indices of habitat specialist (green) and wider countryside species (orange). The long-term linear trends are shown as dotted lines.

16 Excludes non-resident breeding species (i.e. Clouded Yellow, Red Admiral and Painted Lady)

17 Calculations include all species for which long-term population trends were calculated, except for the non-resident breeding species (i.e. Clouded Yellow, Red Admiral and Painted Lady).

Wider countryside butterflies in urban areas

Urban areas typically have little remaining semi-natural habitat. Unsurprisingly, habitat specialist butterflies tend to be rare or absent from towns and cities. However, some wider countryside species are able to persist even in major cities. A study in Greater Manchester found that some butterfly species occurred more commonly as urban density increased (although these were a minority of species)[18], and many wider countryside species have increased their distributions in the more urban parts of Greater London since the 1980s[19]. An assessment of four wider countryside species commonly found in the West Midlands conurbation concluded that the species were able to find and colonise suitable habitat, even in this highly modified landscape[20].

The BNM survey provides an opportunity to examine the effect of urban development on butterfly communities at a wider scale. Detailed butterfly distribution data for 1995–2004 were sub-sampled to reproduce uniform recording effort per 10km square (so as to remove recording effort bias); the resulting species distributions (assessed as the percentage occupancy of 10km squares within the latitudinal range of each species) were compared to a measure of the density of urban development[21] to generate a 'diversity index' for each of the two species groups.

This analysis supports the expected negative relationship between habitat specialists and urbanisation. However, it shows that wider countryside species occur across a range of urban densities and suggests that they are more likely to be recorded in suburban areas than in rural areas with very low urban density. This may reflect not only the positive benefits of the high botanical and structural diversity of suburban gardens[22] and parks, but also the negative impact of the uniformity of intensive agriculture that now dominates many rural landscapes in lowland Britain.

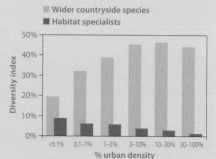

Chart showing an index of species richness (corrected for species range and recording effort) in different urban density bands.

18 Hardy and Dennis 1999

19 Fox and Williams 2006

20 Wood and Pullin 2002

21 Data provided by CEH Monks Wood, derived from the CEH Land Cover Map 2000

22 Smith et al. 2006, in press, Thompson et al. 2003

indications of changes affecting other wildlife and habitats. Further development of UKBMS composite indices will be undertaken with the aim of producing a Populations of Habitat Specialist Butterflies Headline Indicator for the UK Government to complement the existing Wild Bird Index (see Chapter 5).

Taken together, the results confirm that habitat specialists are the more seriously threatened group of butterflies by far. Trends in wider countryside species are more variable; some species are declining while others are expanding rapidly, probably due to climate change.

Causes of change

The recording and monitoring data assembled and analysed for this book present an up-to-date picture of continuing rapid and dramatic change for the butterfly fauna of Britain and Ireland. Most species are in decline, but the populations and distributions of others are increasing.

The chief causes of these changes are familiar and ongoing: continued site destruction, habitat deterioration resulting from unsympathetic management, the additional detrimental effects caused by fragmentation of habitats and butterfly populations, and the opportunities and threats resulting from climate change[23]. The impacts of these factors on butterfly populations are discussed in the next chapter, together with approaches to help stem the declines we have highlighted.

[23] Asher *et al.* 2001, Warren *et al.* 2001a

Chapter 5 **Implications**

Butterflies and habitat loss

The destruction and deterioration of habitats remain primary causes of butterfly declines in Britain and Ireland. Some important butterfly habitats (e.g. early-successional habitats on brownfield sites and late-successional grassland) remain highly vulnerable to land-use change and to management that is unfavourable to threatened butterflies.

Butterflies and other wildlife face many threats, notably from large-scale conversion of habitats to intensive land-uses, abandonment of centuries-old land management practices, and the insidious influences of pollution (including nutrient enrichment) and climate change. Past declines of butterflies in Britain and Ireland have been well documented[1] and mirror butterfly changes across Europe[2] and, indeed, global patterns of biodiversity loss[3]. Analysis of repeated national surveys, including the BNM project, has shown that a greater proportion of British butterfly species (71%) decreased in distribution compared with birds (54%) and vascular plants (28%) over recent decades, suggesting that rates of insect decline are at least as great as those measured and estimated for better-recorded groups such as vertebrates[4].

The analyses in this book confirms the huge decline of butterflies reported previously[5]. However, five additional years of BNM distribution recording and the creation of the UKBMS data set have revealed further serious regional and county-level losses. For example, the Small Blue became extinct in both Northern Ireland and southern Scotland during the 2000–04 period, and the Pearl-bordered Fritillary has been lost from Dorset, Kent and Somerset[6].

Habitat specialist butterflies have continued to fare badly in Britain and Ireland (see p.87) and elsewhere in Europe[7]. Loss of suitable habitat, through destruction or deterioration, remains the primary cause of these declines. The destruction of post-industrial 'brownfield' habitats (though redevelopment or landscaping) was identified as the main cause of rapid rates of loss of inland Dingy Skipper colonies in north-east England (34% loss over the period 1990–2004)[8]. Similarly, extinctions of Large Heath populations in northern Britain appear to be due largely to habitat loss[9]. On the other hand, the main cause of colony extinction of the Marsh Fritillary in England (1990–2000) was the unsuitable management of remaining habitats. Specifically, the decline of traditional extensive livestock grazing in south-west England has radically altered the management regimes of damp pastures and calcareous downland leading, in some instances, to far higher stocking levels and, in others, to agricultural abandonment. Both changes ultimately render habitat unsuitable for the Marsh Fritillary and its larval foodplants[10].

Decreasing management of semi-natural habitats is of considerable conservation concern. Reduced levels of grazing (e.g. through agricultural abandonment, exclusion of livestock/wild herbivores, myxomatosis) and subsequent changes in vegetation structure (particularly succession to scrub) have been linked with the declines of many grassland specialist butterflies including the Adonis Blue and Duke of Burgundy, as well as the Marsh Fritillary[11]. A similar loss of grassland butterflies has been reported in many other European countries[12]. Butterflies that were once characteristic of early-succession conditions within woodland have also declined as traditional woodland management practices (notably coppicing) have been abandoned (e.g. the Pearl-bordered Fritillary, High

1 Asher *et al.* 2001, Emmet and Heath 1990, Fox 2001, Heath *et al.* 1984, Warren 1992
2 Konvicka *et al.* 2006, Maes and Van Dyck 2001, van Swaay and Warren 1999, van Swaay *et al.* 2006
3 Balmford and Bond 2005
4 J.A.Thomas *et al.* 2004
5 Asher *et al.* 2001, Warren *et al.* 2001a
6 Hoare 2006
7 van Swaay *et al.* 2006, Wenzel *et al.* 2006
8 Wainwright 2005, 2006
9 Franco *et al.* in press
10 Hobson *et al.* 2002
11 Bourn and Thomas 2002
12 Konvicka *et al.* 2006, Öckinger *et al.* 2006, van Swaay *et al.* 2006

Brown Fritillary and Heath Fritillary). These changes have caused shifts in the relative importance of different habitats for threatened species. Thus, bracken/grass mosaics are now considered more important than woodland clearings for the High Brown Fritillary, and early-successional habitats on brownfield sites have become important for species such as the Dingy Skipper, Grizzled Skipper, Green Hairstreak and Grayling in some parts of Britain.

Reversing the problems associated with a lack of management is technically possible, although it is made more complex by the effects of landscape fragmentation, eutrophication and climate change. The UKBMS data set provides good examples for practically all species where specific management prescriptions have successfully maintained or increased populations. Conservation can be achieved through reinstating the traditional practices (or modern approximations of them) that originally created and maintained the habitats. A lack of resources is normally the factor limiting conservation of these habitats. Where mechanisms to fund such work have been developed (e.g. higher-tier agri-environment schemes and grants for positive woodland management) significant benefits have been recorded for threatened butterflies[13].

Two habitats currently pose more substantial problems for the conservation of butterflies and other biodiversity. The first of these, brownfield sites, have often become refuges for early-successional butterflies and other insects[14], and for wildlife more generally[15], but do not have a history of traditional agricultural or woodland management. They are under acute threat of destruction through Government policy to focus new building on brownfield sites. Moreover, site location and site conditions (e.g. soil contamination, debris) often render brownfield sites unsuitable for standard habitat management techniques.

The other fresh conservation challenge emerging from our new analysis is the threat to late-successional (often unmanaged) grassland. Such sites have suffered from a perception that they comprise habitats past their best for biodiversity and in need of some active conservation. Often management (e.g. scrub clearance and heavy grazing or mowing) has been reinstated on such grassland to benefit characteristic flora and high-profile species, including butterflies that require short turf, such as the Silver-spotted Skipper. However, such action may be damaging to other threatened butterflies (e.g. the Small Blue and Duke of Burgundy) that require heterogeneous habitats including areas of long vegetation or scrub[16]. Recent research using butterfly transect data in Britain suggested that these butterflies have declined on protected areas such as Sites of Special Scientific Interest (SSSIs)[17] and, ironically, that Government targets to achieve 'favourable status' for SSSIs may be detrimental to some threatened species[18]. A more flexible approach to management is therefore needed to conserve late-successional grassland, which is an important habitat in its own right supporting diverse assemblages of specialist, often threatened, species[19].

The loss and deterioration of habitats remain major threats to butterflies in Britain and Ireland. Until these processes are halted or reversed, the historical and recent declines of most butterfly species will continue and the aims of the Convention of Biological Diversity (e.g. the target to reduce the current rate of biodiversity loss significantly by 2010) will not be achieved here. However, there are some promising signs that agri-environment schemes are slowing the decline of priority butterflies, where these have been especially targeted (see p.98).

Once home to the US Air Force, this former runway at Greenham Common in Berkshire now provides ideal 'brownfield' habitats for the Dingy Skipper, Grizzled Skipper and Grayling.

The Duke of Burgundy has suffered more than most species from changing patterns of habitat management. Most woodland colonies and some grassland ones have been lost or are threatened by the cessation of traditional management. Ironically, other grassland colonies are suffering from intensive management (grazing and scrub clearance) carried out with the aim of conserving biodiversity.

13 Brereton *et al*. 2005, 2006, Warren *et al*. 2001b
14 Benes *et al*. 2003, Fox 2002, Key 2000
15 Gibson 1998, Lunn 2001, Middleton 2000
16 Oates 2000
17 Brereton *et al*. 2006
18 Davies 2005
19 Balmer and Erhardt 2000

Butterflies, fragmentation and landscape-scale conservation

The breeding habitats of many butterflies occupy only small fragments of the modern landscape. Metapopulation theory suggests that species will not survive on individual fragments, but require networks of sites between which they can move. Landscape-scale conservation seeks to maintain or create such networks and so ensure the long-term survival of threatened butterflies.

In the highly-modified landscape of Britain and Ireland, many butterflies are restricted now to the remaining fragments of semi-natural habitat. This is most evident with habitat specialist species, which are confined to particular habitats (e.g. unimproved calcareous grassland, lowland heath), but also appears to be increasingly true of certain wider countryside species (e.g. the Small Heath and Common Blue), at least in some regions. Whilst the quality of habitat fragments remains a vital factor in determining the survival of butterfly colonies[20] (and conservation management should always seek to understand[21] and maximise habitat quality), the size and degree of isolation of fragments also influence long-term persistence[22]. Thus habitat fragmentation may itself cause the eventual extinction of butterfly colonies on those patches of apparently suitable habitat that remain[23].

Metapopulation theory is a recent ecological concept that was developed partly using butterflies as a model group and which has been widely applied to explain butterfly distribution and changing status[24]. The metapopulation concept is that species persist in a landscape as a dynamic collection of interlinked colonies on patches of suitable habitat. The species exists as a population of populations – a metapopulation. A colony on a particular patch may become extinct, perhaps by accident (e.g. fire, extreme weather event, disease) or perhaps because the habitat gradually becomes unsuitable (e.g. through succession or changing land-use), but providing that other colonies in the metapopulation remain nearby, the patch can be recolonised in due course, when conditions improve. Field observations have shown rapid rates of colony extinction and recolonisation (e.g. for the Glanville Fritillary in Finland) and that these dynamics affect most colonies in fragmented landscapes (e.g. the Silver-studded Blue in Britain)[25]. Metapopulation models make important predictions for the conservation of existing colonies and for habitat restoration. Specifically, they show that colonies on large patches of habitat are less likely to become extinct because populations are large and, perhaps, because such habitats are more varied. They also predict that empty patches close to occupied patches are more likely to be recolonised than distant ones because few butterflies fly long distances.

Many threatened British butterflies appear to conform to the metapopulation concept (e.g. the Lulworth Skipper, Silver-spotted Skipper, Silver-studded Blue, Adonis Blue, Glanville Fritillary, Heath Fritillary)[26] and metapopulation theory has been used for population viability assessments and to help guide conservation action. For example, the remaining population networks of the Marsh Fritillary in England and Wales have been modelled as metapopulations to predict whether they are viable in the long-term. Most of the networks in Wales, the one remaining in Cumbria and several others in England were deemed insufficient for long-term survival without the restoration of substantial amounts of additional habitat[27]. Similar findings have been reported for the Marsh Fritillary and other butterfly species in continental Europe[28]. Formerly occupied networks have also been examined to assess the potential for reintroductions (e.g. the Duke of Burgundy in north Wales, Marsh Fritillary in England and Wales)[29].

Such assessments not only indicate the probability of long-term persistence of metapopulations in the landscape, but can also be used to measure the relative contribution of specific habitat fragments. For example, the current network of protected areas (SSSIs and nature reserves) was deemed insufficient to guarantee

20 Bourn *et al.* 2002, Dennis and Eales 1997, Fleishman *et al.* 2002, Krauss *et al.* 2004, 2005, J.A.Thomas *et al.* 2001

21 Dennis *et al.* 2003

22 Thomas *et al.* 1998, Wilson *et al.* 2002

23 Hanski 2003

24 Hanski 1999, Hanski 2003

25 Hanski 1999, C.D.Thomas *et al.* 2001b

26 Davies *et al.* 2005, Hill *et al.* 1996, Thomas *et al.* 1992, J.A. Thomas *et al.* 2001

27 Bulman 2001

28 e.g. Bergman and Kindvall 2004, Schtickzelle *et al.* 2005

29 Bulman 2001, León-Cortés *et al.* 2003

Habitats for threatened butterflies, such as the unimproved grassland on the hilltop in the centre of this picture, have been reduced and fragmented by intensive agriculture and other land uses. Butterfly colonies are at increased risk of extinction as a result.

the long-term survival of a Dingy Skipper metapopulation in north Wales, if unprotected habitats (mainly on brownfield sites) were destroyed[30]. An exciting extension of this approach has been used to classify the entire British landscape according to relative importance for all butterflies, thus identifying priority areas for the conservation of the whole butterfly fauna[31].

New landscape-scale conservation initiatives are helping to conserve Marsh Fritillary metapopulations in Britain.

The recent shift towards landscape-scale conservation of butterflies in Britain also owes much to the metapopulation concept. This approach promotes the management of functional landscapes in order to maintain or restore effective metapopulations. Landscape-scale projects typically attempt to link key habitat fragments together both physically (i.e. improving connections between them through habitat recreation) and by co-ordinating management across sites. Identifying key sites for long-term survival and recognising the dispersal ability of the butterfly species involved enable effective targeting of conservation effort and resources[32].

Landscape-scale projects are now central to the strategy being developed by Butterfly Conservation and its partners to conserve threatened species in the UK. Among the landscape-scale projects currently underway are Marsh Fritillary projects on Salisbury Plain, the culm grasslands of Devon, wet grasslands on Dartmoor and Exmoor, the moors of mid-Cornwall and the rhos pastures of Carmarthenshire, High Brown Fritillary on the Morecambe Bay Limestones, Silver-studded Blue on the Suffolk Sandlings, and the Pearl-bordered Fritillary and Small Pearl-bordered Fritillary in the woodlands of Surrey and Sussex[33]. Agri-environment schemes also operate at the landscape scale (provided that sufficient landowners participate in them) and, if suitably targeted, will complement biodiversity conservation projects. As well as promoting the continued survival of threatened butterflies under current conditions, improving connections between semi-natural habitats in the fragmented landscape will maximise the ability of the species to withstand future environmental change. These measures are also likely to benefit many other insects that occur in the same habitats, as well as sustaining the local character and attractiveness of the countryside.

30 Gutiérrez 2005
31 Moilanen et al. 2005
32 Davies et al. 2005
33 Bulman 2005, Davis and Corbett 2004, McKernan 2004, Sazer 2004

Butterflies and climate change

Butterflies are already responding to climate change by altering their phenology, ranges and ecology. Although most responses have been favourable thus far, predictive modelling suggests that climate change will become a significant cause of butterfly decline during this century.

The climate is changing[34] and species across the world are responding[35]. Climate change may bring opportunities for some species as well as threats, but grave concerns have been raised about the overall impact on biodiversity and ecosystems[36]. It is important for biodiversity policy, as well as for scientific understanding, that the effects of climate change are assessed.

Butterflies, cultural icons of summertime, have been a focus of efforts to chart and predict climatic effects on biodiversity[37]. As 'cold-blooded' animals, their rate of development, physiology, behaviour, ecology and reproductive success are all directly affected by climate[38].

The effect of climate on butterfly population size has been demonstrated clearly using British monitoring data[39] and researchers have found many species-specific examples of climatic influence on ecological and life history traits[40]. In Britain, most butterflies reach a climate-induced limit to their range (either a northern or southern range margin) and many show local adaptation to less than ideal climatic conditions. They may occupy restricted niches (e.g. the Silver-spotted Skipper, Heath Fritillary), have longer life cycles (e.g. the Common Blue) or be restricted to a narrower range of larval foodplants (e.g. the Swallowtail) than in warmer parts of their European range[41].

A wide range of climate change impacts has already been demonstrated for butterflies. Such impacts are seen most readily at species' range margins. Expansions and contractions of species' historical ranges that are consistent with a climate change explanation (i.e. shifts of range margins to higher latitude and altitude) have been documented for butterflies at within-country[42], national[43] and international scales[44]. In Britain, northward extensions of range margins have been identified from the BNM data for 11 'southern' butterflies (c. 25% of species with a northern limit)[45] and evidence found for range contractions to higher latitudes and altitudes amongst three (Northern Brown Argus, Mountain Ringlet and Scotch Argus) of the four species with southern range margins[46]. Altitudinal shifts have also been recorded for butterflies in other parts of Europe and in North America[47].

Modelling of butterfly distributions and climate variables has increased confidence that these observed changes in species' distributions are not only consistent with those predicted from climate change, but are a genuine response to it[48]. Such models have also been used to predict the future ranges of butterflies in Britain and across Europe under different scenarios of climate change. The results warn of severe declines not just for 'northern' species but, when realistic assumptions of habitat availability and butterfly dispersal are incorporated, also for many 'southern' species that are reliant on semi-natural habitats[49]. The distributions of many butterflies in Britain, even wider countryside species such as the Speckled Wood, are lagging behind climatic changes because of habitat loss and fragmentation[50]. Nevertheless, as demonstrated in this book, many 'southern' wider countryside butterflies seem to have benefited from climate change in Britain over recent decades, increasing both their distributions and population levels at monitored sites (e.g. the Peacock, Comma and Ringlet)[51]. In addition, whilst no new butterflies have colonised Britain or Ireland during the current period of rapid human-induced climate change, two migrant species that have bred here regularly during the summer months (the Clouded Yellow and Red Admiral) now appear capable of successful overwintering and may therefore be in the process of becoming resident species[52]. The distributions of all these species, colonising migrants and 'southern' wider countryside residents, are expected to continue increasing over the next decade or two.

Past losses of Large Heath colonies have been attributed to habitat destruction (e.g. drainage, afforestation) but climate change is predicted to render most of Britain and Ireland unsuitable for the butterfly by the end of the century.

34 IPCC 2001, King 2005

35 Hickling *et al.* 2006, McCarty 2001, Parmesan and Yohe 2003, Root *et al.* 2003

36 Schröter *et al.* 2005, Stefanescu *et al.* 2004, C.D. Thomas *et al.* 2004

37 Parmesan 2003

38 Dennis 1993

39 Brereton *et al.* 2006, Pollard 1988, Pollard and Yates 1993, Roy *et al.* 2001

40 e.g. Bryant *et al.* 2002, Burke *et al.* 2005, Parmesan 2003, Roy and Thomas 2003, Sparks *et al.* 2005

41 see Asher *et al.* 2001 for examples

42 Crozier 2003, Wilson *et al.* 2005

43 Fox *et al.* 2001b, Konvicka *et al.* 2003, Warren *et al.* 2001a

44 Burton 2001, Parmesan 1996, Parmesan *et al.* 1999

45 Hill *et al.* 2002

46 Franco *et al.* in press

47 Konvicka *et al.* 2003, Parmesan 1996, Wilson *et al.* 2005

48 Hill *et al.* 1999, Warren *et al.* 2001a

49 Berry *et al.* 2002, Hill *et al.* 2002

50 Hill *et al.* 2001, Menéndez *et al.* in press

51 Warren *et al.* 2001a

52 Asher *et al.* 2001, Dennis *et al.* 2006b, Skelton 2003

The established relationships between climate and butterfly abundance in Britain, derived from transect monitoring, have also been modelled to predict future population changes. Most species increased in abundance in the simulations (e.g. the Common Blue, Marbled White and Gatekeeper), whilst others remained stable (e.g. the Grizzled Skipper and Wall) and only the Large White was predicted to decline[53].

Another well-documented set of climate change impacts on butterflies is in their phenology (the timing of life cycle events). Almost all British butterflies are flying earlier in the year now than in the 1970s (first sighting and peak flight date), and many now enjoy longer flight periods[54]. For example, the average first annual sighting of an Orange-tip on butterfly transects was 18 days earlier in 1998 compared with 1976. Similar advances in flight period have been demonstrated for butterflies at lower latitudes, away from their range margins[55]. Unusual phenological events are increasingly being documented for butterflies in Britain (e.g. overwintering Large White larvae, second broods of Purple Emperor and Peacock, all mentioned in the species accounts) and elsewhere[56].

Finally, recent studies of butterflies have provided examples of the mechanisms by which organisms respond, favourably or adversely, to climate change. In Britain, climate change between 1982 and 2000 substantially increased the amount of calcareous grassland that was suitable as breeding habitat for the Silver-spotted Skipper. As a result of the warming climate, the butterfly was no longer dependent upon the hottest, short-turf, south-facing habitats, but could start to breed in both slightly longer turf and on cooler aspects[57]. Thus climate change is viewed as a major reason for the recovery of the Silver-spotted Skipper, though the introduction of beneficial grazing regimes to conserve downland biodiversity has also played a part. Similar responses to climate change have been predicted for the Silver-studded Blue and a range of other heathland organisms[58]. In contrast, in California, two colonies of the threatened Bay Checkerspot (*Euphydryas editha bayensis*) are thought to have been driven to extinction by recent climate change. More extreme fluctuations in annual rainfall (as predicted by climate change models) appeared to reduce the time period in which foodplants were available to larvae of this butterfly, and thus increased larval mortality through starvation[59].

Butterflies provide an excellent 'model' group for the study and assessment of climate change effects in Britain and Ireland. Butterflies are highly sensitive to climate and many signals of climate change have already been elucidated from the comprehensive baseline data that exist for this group. In addition, predictive modelling has been developed. Above all, the responses of butterflies to past and future climate change are likely to be mirrored amongst our biodiversity as a whole, particularly other invertebrates.

53 Roy *et al.* 2001
54 Roy and Sparks 2000
55 Forister and Shapiro 2003
56 e.g. Dell *et al.* 2005
57 Davies *et al.* 2005, 2006, C.D. Thomas *et al.* 2001a
58 Thomas *et al.* 1999
59 McLaughlin *et al.* 2002

A warmer climate has benefited the Silver-spotted Skipper by reducing its reliance upon south-facing slopes with very short turf.

Butterflies as indicators

> For a range of biological and practical reasons, butterflies have great potential as indicators of environmental change and its impacts on biodiversity as a whole. Butterfly population data are being used increasingly to measure the success of biodiversity conservation policies.

There is insufficient knowledge of the distribution and abundance of most species in the world to support their conservation. Even in Britain, which has probably the best-studied insect fauna[60], the assessment of priority and implementation of conservation action are hampered by insufficient data. Because of this problem, ecologists have sought species or groups of species that can be used as indicators for overall species richness, for assessing habitat quality and for measuring the consequences of environmental change. Indicator species would be extremely useful in conservation planning (e.g. in selecting protected areas) and much effort has been expended in the search for such taxa. Butterflies have been recognised as potentially valuable indicators, both for their rapid and sensitive responses to subtle habitat or climatic changes and as representatives for the diversity and responses of other wildlife[61].

There are several reasons why butterflies make effective indicators, particularly in Britain. First and foremost, there are excellent data sets detailing past and present distribution, population size and phenology. These data sources rival those for the best-studied groups such as birds and exceed those available for other insect and invertebrate groups[62].

Secondly, many aspects of butterfly biology predispose them to be sensitive to, and react rapidly to, changes in their environment[63]. Short life cycles mean that butterflies react quickly, whilst the limited dispersal ability, larval foodplant specialisation and close-reliance on the weather and climate make many butterfly species sensitive to fine-scale changes. Butterflies occur in all main terrestrial habitat types and almost all stages of succession in Britain and Ireland, so they have the potential to act as indicators for a wide range of species and habitats (the obvious exception being dead wood (saproxylic) species). Recent reviews have concluded that butterflies are reasonable, albeit imperfect, representatives of other terrestrial invertebrates[64]. Nevertheless, we recognise that there are limitations. For example, in Britain and Ireland, butterflies are a small group of herbivorous species and other species might be better indicators for invertebrate groups that are predominantly predators or parasitoids. The difficulty lies in finding species that are sufficiently well studied and comprehensively recorded to fulfil the role!

Finally, because insects make up the largest proportion of terrestrial wildlife, both in Britain and Ireland, and globally, it is crucial that we assess the fate of insect groups in order to monitor the overall state of biodiversity. Being insects, the responses seen in butterflies are more likely to reflect parallel, often unquantified, changes amongst other insect groups, and thus the majority of biodiversity, than established indicators such as those based on birds. This representativeness has been demonstrated in recent studies[65]. Furthermore, as with many other insects, a high proportion of butterfly species are restricted in Britain to specific micro-habitats in relatively small areas of semi-natural habitat. Subtle changes in these habitats may substantially diminish insect diversity, but may not impact significantly upon higher trophic levels (e.g. bird populations) currently used as biodiversity indicators, or the impact on higher levels may be delayed[66].

The distribution of butterflies has been found repeatedly to predict the occurrence of other species, areas of high biodiversity, and habitat quality[67], although there are some unsuccessful examples too[68]. The responses of butterflies to environmental change, including habitat loss and climate change, also appear to be similar to those of other taxa[69]. As bioindicators responding to climate change, butterflies are currently in a league of their own because of their sensitivity and the availability of extensive data sets (see p.94)[70].

60 Collins and Thomas 1991

61 Oostermeijer and van Swaay 1998, Parmesan 2003, Thomas 2005

62 Thomas 2005

63 Hilty and Merenlender 2000

64 Ehrlich 1994, Thomas 2005

65 Conrad *et al.* in press, Hickling *et al.* 2006, Thomas and Clarke 2004, J.A.Thomas *et al.* 2004

66 Thomas 1995

67 Beccaloni and Gaston 1995, Brown 1991, Brown and Freitas 2000, Fleishman *et al.* 2005, Kerr *et al.* 2000, Maes and van Dyck 2005, Maes *et al.* 2005

68 Grill *et al.* 2005, Kremen *et al.* 2003, Ricketts *et al.* 2002

69 Conrad *et al.* in press, Hickling *et al.* 2006, Parmesan and Yohe 2003, J.A.Thomas *et al.* 2004

70 Parmesan 2003, Thomas 2005

In addition to the scientific relevance of butterfly trends, butterflies are of great value in assessing the success of policies for sustaining biodiversity. Governments, in the UK and elsewhere, have made commitments to sustainable development and biodiversity protection, including the ambitious target of the UN Convention on Biological Diversity to achieve a significant reduction of the current rate of biodiversity loss by 2010. Indicators are vital in monitoring progress towards such aims and targets, but only a limited number of indicators have been developed in the UK thus far and none focus on terrestrial insects[71].

As part of the current development of the UKBMS (see Chapter 1 for details), Butterfly Conservation and CEH will create a range of policy-relevant biodiversity indicators suitable for Governmental use at UK and country levels, and within some major policy workstreams (farmland, forestry etc). Most important within these will be a UK headline indicator to complement the 'Quality of Life' indicator based on populations of wild birds that is already in use. There is no guarantee that a butterfly indicator would be adopted officially by the Government, but a headline indicator, based on butterfly population trends, will bring many benefits including popular appeal, representation of the very large part of our biodiversity that is made up of terrestrial insects, and better monitoring of some UK BAP habitat types. The latter include open semi-natural habitats (e.g. grassland, heathland, woodland clearings, coastal) and other early-successional habitats (e.g. post-industrial 'brownfield' sites) that are especially important for invertebrates.

The Adonis Blue is one of a number of habitat specialist butterflies used to develop pilot biodiversity indicators from transect data at European Union, UK and country levels.

Butterfly data are also being used to develop pan-European indicators to enable the European Union to monitor progress towards the 2010 target. Butterflies form a substantial part of a multi-taxon indicator that has been trialled[72] and work is underway to use transect data from the UK and eight other countries to create a specific European butterfly index. A trial grassland butterfly index based upon population levels of 17 butterfly species (ranging from specialists such as the Lulworth Skipper, Adonis Blue and Marsh Fritillary, to generalists including the Large Skipper, Common Blue and Wall) showed a dramatic decrease across Europe of almost 50% over 15 years (1990–2004)[73].

Thanks in large part to the comprehensive data sets generated by population monitoring and distribution recording, butterflies make effective indicators of environmental quality and change. They have a key role to play in addressing some of the most pressing questions in ecological research[74]. A broad base of indicators is required to monitor biodiversity adequately and several composite indices based on butterfly data are now in development at national and international scales. These will complement existing indicators and will have important policy applications in the near future. The butterfly population trends that form the basis of these indicators are published for the first time in this book.

71 Defra 2002
72 de Heer *et al.* 2005
73 van Swaay and van Strien 2005
74 Sutherland *et al.* in press

Butterflies and agri-environment schemes

Many butterflies, threatened and common species alike, rely on traditional agricultural practices. Agri-environment schemes designed to maintain or reinstate appropriate management have benefited target butterfly species in England. It is hoped that the new generation of schemes will bring further improvements for a wider range of butterflies.

We live in an increasingly urbanised society, yet the UK remains largely an agricultural landscape, with approximately three-quarters of the 24 million hectare land surface used for agricultural production. Farmland provides extremely important habitats for butterflies: more than 90% of Britain's resident species breed on farmland over at least part of their range, with semi-natural farmland habitats being particularly important[75].

The results presented in this book confirm that butterflies, much like other wildlife[76], have suffered acute declines across farmland landscapes in recent decades. To counter these biodiversity losses, the UK Government is one of 26 European countries to have developed an agri-environment programme, part-funded by the European Union (EU)[77]. In 2003, an estimated £2.5 billion was spent on such schemes across the EU. In England, two main schemes have operated: Environmentally Sensitive Areas (ESAs) and the Countryside Stewardship Scheme (CSS), which collectively have brought nearly 470,000 hectares of land into environmental management[78]. Both schemes were replaced in 2005 by Environmental Stewardship (ES) comprised of three elements; Higher Level Environmental Stewardship (HLS), Entry Level Stewardship (ELS) and Organic Entry Level Stewardship (OELS). ES has a budget of £150 million a year, which is expected to more than double within the next few years.

Given the levels of public funding agri-environment schemes receive, it is important that they deliver environmental benefits. In recent years, Defra and other organisations have completed a number of detailed environmental research and monitoring programmes for these schemes, focusing on botanical communities and birds[79]. Butterfly Conservation has provided a much-needed addition to this assessment, researching impacts on butterflies utilising the UKBMS data set. This research indicates that schemes have failed to halt the general decline of butterflies on farmland[80]. The study found that for 40 butterfly species assessed at over 300 agri-environment scheme sites, there had been a significant decline in mean abundance of more than 20% over the last 10 years. This was part of a general decline of butterflies on farmland habitats, including those protected as SSSIs and across the wider countryside.

However, there was some cause for optimism. The eight UK BAP Priority Species studied fared better overall at sites entered into agri-environment schemes than elsewhere[80]. Agri-environment schemes had helped to slow and, in some cases, reverse the declines (e.g. for the Silver-spotted Skipper and Adonis Blue). The improvements were attributed mainly to the targeted measures undertaken for Priority Species on a large number of sites, instigated by the UK BAP process and delivered by agri-environment scheme payments. They also show that the extensive advisory work provided by Butterfly Conservation and other conservation bodies to land managers and conservation advisors has made a measurable difference in helping to conserve threatened butterflies.

In north-west England for example, great efforts have been made to manage bracken slopes and rocky limestone grasslands to benefit the High Brown Fritillary. More than half of the remaining sites supporting this threatened butterfly have been entered into carefully targeted CSS or Lake District ESA agri-environment scheme agreements. High Brown Fritillary populations have responded positively to the subsequent habitat management. As a consequence, the butterfly's population is stable overall in this region, due largely to the favourable trend on

75 Brereton 2004
76 Benton et al. 2002, Robinson and Sutherland 2002
77 Kleijn and Sutherland 2003
78 Ovenden et al. 1998
79 Critchley et al. 2004, Ecoscope/CPM/CJC Consulting 2003
80 Brereton et al. 2005

scheme sites (there has been an overall decline at non-scheme sites). The trend in north-west England is in stark contrast to other regions in the UK, where many remaining colonies are on common land and conservation action has proved harder to implement successfully[81].

The agri-environment scheme research also looked at trends in butterfly abundance according to sward structure requirements. It found that the species benefiting most from schemes were those associated with botanically-rich short and medium turf conditions[81]. In contrast, butterflies benefiting least were those that require taller grass, variable turf structure and scrub edge/mosaic habitats. These included threatened species such as the Small Blue and Duke of Burgundy. The results reflect the fact that, all too often, semi-natural habitats in agri-environment schemes have been managed uniformly for their general botanical interest, without tailoring management sufficiently to benefit individual species of high conservation value. This is a particular problem for many invertebrates that require fine-scale habitat heterogeneity.

The results of this butterfly research in England complement the findings of other studies across Europe. These have reported that agri-environment schemes have had a moderately positive, albeit mixed, impact in conserving farmland biodiversity[82], with carefully tailored schemes producing some very beneficial effects for individual species[83].

Farmers have been managing land primarily for food production for several thousand years, yet the concept of managing farmland to produce environmental benefits through incentive schemes is less than 20 years old. The first agri-environment schemes have, to a large degree, been land management trials on an extensive scale, and important lessons have been learnt. Butterfly Conservation has worked closely with Defra on the design of the new Environmental Stewardship Scheme, especially HLS which is orientated more towards managing sites for a broader range of interest features (including species) and has greater flexibility in management prescriptions than the earlier schemes[84]. These attributes should bring further benefits for threatened butterflies in future.

The extent to which butterflies can be conserved effectively on farmland depends not only on how we manage our 'special sites', but also on the way we manage the countryside as a whole. The most exciting new feature of Environmental Stewardship is that, through the ELS element, all farmers and landowners will be able to apply for funding to carry out positive environmental management. This is reflected in the Government target of bringing 60% of farmland into schemes by 2007. The landscape scale of operation offers perhaps the greatest hope of reversing the fragmentation of habitats rich in butterflies and other wildlife that has occurred across our farmland landscape[85].

Only time will tell if Environmental Stewardship helps to deliver the long hoped for recovery of our dwindling butterfly populations. Through the UKBMS project, Butterfly Conservation, CEH and JNCC are developing efficient and cost-effective ways of monitoring the impacts on butterflies of Environmental Stewardship and equivalent agri-environment schemes in Northern Ireland, Scotland and Wales. In the UKBMS, the transect network will increasingly focus on monitoring habitat specialist butterflies on semi-natural habitats, whilst a new method (most likely based on random sampling) will be developed to monitor more effectively the abundance of common and widespread butterflies across the whole landscape. For the UKBMS to be effective, it will (like all our recording schemes) rely on both the current and future generations of skilled and dedicated volunteer recorders, rising to the challenge and getting involved.

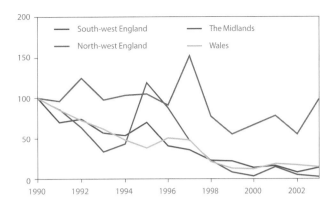

Data from the UKBMS show that the High Brown Fritillary population has been maintained over the period of agri-environment schemes in north-west England (1990–2003), in contrast to other regions where the butterfly has declined severely.

Agri-environment scheme payments can help landowners to restore or maintain grazing to conserve threatened butterflies and other biodiversity. In this case, low-intensity cattle gazing produces a tussocky sward that benefits the Lulworth Skipper and Small Blue, both candidate UK BAP Priority Species.

81 Brereton et al. 2005
82 Kleijn et al. 2006, Knop et al. 2006
83 Peach et al. 2001, Vickery et al. 2004
84 Smallshire et al. 2004
85 Donald and Evans 2006

Butterflies and the UK Biodiversity Action Plan

> Threatened butterflies can be targeted for action under the UK Biodiversity Action Plan thanks to comprehensive distribution and population data. A total of 16 butterflies have been proposed as new Priority Species in the 2006 review of the plan.

Resources for biodiversity conservation are always scarce, competing with many other demands for public funds. Therefore, it is vital that these limited resources are utilised wisely and effectively, by giving priority to those species, habitats and sites that are most threatened. The BNM distribution records and, more recently, the UKBMS population monitoring data provide the means to prioritise and target the conservation of butterflies.

Over the last decade, the allocation of resources and prioritisation of biodiversity action in the UK have been guided by the UK Biodiversity Action Plan (UK BAP). This initiative was developed by the Government to meet its commitments under the Convention on Biological Diversity, which was signed at Rio de Janeiro in 1992. Species and habitats are afforded levels of official priority within the UK BAP, according to objective criteria (e.g. rates of decline or international rarity) and to pragmatic decisions about what actions and targets are attainable. The UK BAP has cascaded down from the UK Parliament to the devolved national authorities and to local government. A hierarchy of biodiversity action plans now exists (or is in development) for most areas and this has led to increased awareness and additional resources for survey, monitoring, research and conservation of threatened butterflies.

Prior to the UK BAP, butterflies had been assigned to threat categories in the *British Insect Red Data Book*[86] and, more recently, in a new red list that included rate of decline as a criterion of threat[87]. Distribution records published in the *Atlas of Butterflies in Britain and Ireland*[88], which are now included in the BNM data set, formed the basis for this new listing and fed, in turn, into the initial selection of butterfly species for the UK BAP. The UK BAP originally included 11 butterflies as Priority Species (the highest level of importance), with a further 14 at the lesser tier of Species of Conservation Concern[89].

Thus, prioritising conservation efforts for butterflies in the UK has, for many years, relied on assessments of changing species distribution derived from butterfly records. Although Britain has probably the best historical record of butterfly distributions for any country, such assessments are not without problems. The spatial scale at which change is measured[90], variation in recording effort and coverage, and recording bias (taxonomic, ecological, geographical and temporal) may all potentially distort the results[91]. Thankfully, butterflies are sufficiently well recorded and these potential problems have been sufficiently investigated that there is a high level of confidence in recent assessments of distribution change. Furthermore, other data sources and analytical approaches have corroborated the findings[92].

The Priority Species listed within the UK BAP are currently being reviewed and butterflies and other taxa have been assessed against objective criteria[93]. New information on butterfly priorities has been derived by an advanced sub-sampling analysis of the BNM data[94] combined, for the first time, with trends from the new UKBMS data set, based on transect data from over 1,000 sites (see Chapter 2). Thus, for most butterflies, both population and distribution trends have been assessed against the UK BAP criteria, giving more certainty of identifying species that are in rapid decline[95].

From these analyses, as well as from knowledge of international threat levels[96] and other factors (e.g. threats from climate or land-use change), Butterfly Conservation advocated retaining eight of the existing Priority Species and proposed 16 additional butterflies as new Priority Species in the UK BAP review[97]. The addition of so many new priority butterflies will need to be accompanied by a

86 Shirt 1987
87 Warren *et al.* 1997
88 Heath *et al.* 1984
89 UK Biodiversity Group 1998
90 Cowley *et al.* 1999, Thomas and Abery 1995
91 Dennis *et al.* 1999, 2006a, Dennis and Thomas 2000
92 Warren *et al.* 2001a
93 Buglife 2004
94 Warren *et al.* 2001a
95 Bourn *et al.* 2005
96 van Swaay and Warren 1999
97 Bourn *et al.* 2005

Summary of 2006 UK BAP Priority Review butterfly species and their qualification criteria. Adapted from Bourn *et al*. 2005.

	Reasons for qualification	Distribution change(BNM) % change 1970–82 vs 1995–2004*	Population change (UKBMS) Long-term % change**	Population change (UKBMS) 10-year % change 1995–2004
Species to remain Priority				
Chequered Skipper	Severe decline in range, no evidence of recovery	-38	–	–
Silver-studded Blue	Severe decline in range and abundance	-43	-1	-72
Northern Brown Argus	Localised species, no evidence of recovery, threat from climate change	+18	-10	-30
Large Blue	Internationally threatened, extinct in UK and being re-introduced	-100	–	–
Pearl-bordered Fritillary	Severe decline in range and abundance	-61	-66	-51
High Brown Fritillary	Severe decline in range and abundance	-79	-13	-85
Marsh Fritillary	Internationally threatened, severe decline in range and abundance	-46	-73	+73
Heath Fritillary	Severe decline in abundance	-25	-73	-46
Proposed additions as Priority Species				
Lulworth Skipper	Internationally threatened	-15	-13	+79
Dingy Skipper	Severe decline in range	-48	-37	-26
Grizzled Skipper	Severe decline in range	-49	-34	-42
Wood White	Severe decline in range and abundance	-65	-64	+10
Brown Hairstreak	Severe decline in range	-43	–	–
White-letter Hairstreak	Severe decline in range and abundance	-53	-71	-63
Small Blue	Severe decline in range	-38	-6	+121
Duke of Burgundy	Severe decline in range and abundance	-52	-28	-58
White Admiral	Severe decline in abundance	-31	-62	-36
Small Pearl-bordered Fritillary	Severe decline in range and abundance	-34	-70	-10
Glanville Fritillary	Extreme rarity and threat, especially from climate change	-17	–	–
Wall	Severe decline in range and abundance	-38	-65	-2
Mountain Ringlet	Extreme threat from climate change (evidence of decline at low altitudes)	-12	–	–
Grayling	Severe decline in range and abundance	-45	-51	-41
Small Heath	Severe decline in abundance	-29	-52	-29
Large Heath	Severe decline in range	-43	-26	+58
Proposed demotion to Species of Conservation Concern				
Silver-spotted Skipper	Large increase in abundance, some recovery of range	+4	+1,524	+2
Large Copper	Extinct in the UK	–	–	–
Adonis Blue	Increase in abundance	-19	+28	+63

* Distribution decline underestimates population losses; the threshold for 50% population decline is estimated to be 32% loss at the 10km square scale.

** Trends are for 1976–2004 except Wood White 1977–2004; Small Blue, High Brown Fritillary and Large Heath 1978–2004; Silver-spotted Skipper, Silver-studded Blue, Northern Brown Argus, Adonis Blue and Duke of Burgundy 1979–2004; Brown Hairstreak and Marsh Fritillary 1983–2004; Heath Fritillary 1984–2004; Lulworth Skipper 1992–2004.

parallel increase in resources if the success of the UK BAP process is to be maintained. Some of these new candidate species have long been recognised as of conservation concern (e.g. the Duke of Burgundy), but the recent declines of most (e.g. the Dingy Skipper and Grayling) would have been almost unimaginable to entomologists a generation ago. The proposals and supporting justification are given in the table (above). Three species have been proposed for downgrading from Priority Species to Species of Conservation Concern: the Large Copper because it is extinct and the Silver-spotted Skipper and Adonis Blue because of their improving status over recent years.

The recording and monitoring data gathered for butterfly distributions and populations enable precise, objective and cost-effective assessments of conservation priorities for the UK Biodiversity Action Plan, and for the national,

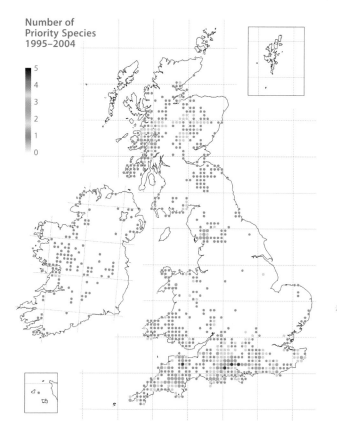

Number of
Priority Species
1995–2004

5
4
3
2
1
0

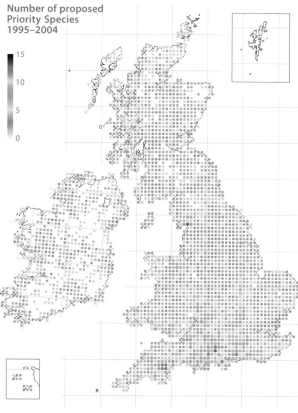

Number of proposed
Priority Species
1995–2004

15

10

5

0

The 1995–2004 BNM distribution of existing UK BAP Priority Species of butterflies: Chequered Skipper, Silver-spotted Skipper, Silver-studded Blue, Northern Brown Argus, Adonis Blue, Large Blue, Pearl-bordered Fritillary, High Brown Fritillary, Marsh Fritillary, Heath Fritillary. The Large Copper is extinct and does not contribute to the map

The 1995–2004 BNM distribution of proposed UK BAP Priority Species of butterflies: Chequered Skipper, Lulworth Skipper, Dingy Skipper, Grizzled Skipper, Wood White, Brown Hairstreak, White-letter Hairstreak, Small Blue, Silver-studded Blue, Northern Brown Argus, Large Blue, Duke of Burgundy, White Admiral, Small Pearl-bordered Fritillary, Pearl-bordered Fritillary, High Brown Fritillary, Marsh Fritillary, Glanville Fritillary, Heath Fritillary, Wall, Mountain Ringlet, Grayling, Small Heath, Large Heath. The map does not show 'wood white' records in Ireland.

regional and local plans that stem from it. The same data also allow progress towards the targets in these plans to be measured. The development of the UKBMS is particularly important in this regard[98], because the population status of UK BAP priority butterflies can now be reported annually from the transect monitoring network. This is a major improvement on the five-year or longer assessment periods based upon BNM distribution recording and specific species' surveys.

98 Brereton *et al.* 2006

Chapter 6 **Conclusions**

The development of a greatly expanded butterfly monitoring system (the UKBMS) and continued recording as part of the Butterflies for the New Millennium (BNM) project have provided data sets of enormous importance for biodiversity conservation and sustainable development. Distribution records show the location of scarce and threatened species, while transect data enable the impact of habitat management techniques to be assessed objectively. Both sources of information are crucial to ensure the effective targeting of limited conservation resources. These data sets also allow butterflies to be used as indicators of the effectiveness of Government policies and of the impacts on biodiversity of changes to the environment and climate. The organisations that co-ordinate and fund butterfly recording and monitoring and, especially, the thousands of volunteers who carry out the work on the ground can take pride in these major achievements.

The globally endangered Large Blue has been reintroduced to Britain following extinction in 1979. In 2004, an estimated 7,000 Large Blues flew in Britain. This success is due to the dedication of a large partnership of conservation organisations and individuals, helped considerably by the UK Biodiversity Action Plan process.

Although these data sets are amongst the best in the world, we can take little pride in the overall state of our butterflies in the early years of this new century. The analyses presented in this book reiterate the rapid declines revealed by *The Millennium Atlas of Butterflies in Britain and Ireland* five years ago. The scale of the challenge is daunting, exemplified by the qualification of so many additional butterfly species (including wider countryside species) for the revised UK Biodiversity Action Plan.

Nevertheless, we can perhaps be more optimistic about the future than was possible five years ago. Many landscape-scale habitat conservation and restoration projects have been initiated in the last few years and will undoubtedly benefit threatened butterflies. New mass-participation agri-environment schemes and better-targeted management of semi-natural farmland habitats also have the potential to reverse some of the damage caused by intensification and neglect over recent decades.

The butterflies themselves are the ultimate arbiters of conservation success or failure. The national resurgence of the Silver-spotted Skipper and Adonis Blue, the ongoing success of the Large Blue reintroduction programme and the regional recoveries of species such as the Wood White, High Brown Fritillary and Heath Fritillary are significant successes that should be celebrated. These positive outcomes demonstrate that it is possible to conserve even the most threatened butterflies, given sufficient knowledge, will and resources. Concerted effort to address key issues (highlighted in the box overleaf) must continue during the next five years to secure a lasting future for Britain and Ireland's butterflies and biodiversity as a whole.

A 10-point plan for the conservation of butterflies revisited: An assessment of progress over the past five years

The 10-point plan was conceived for *The Millennium Atlas of Butterflies in Britain and Ireland*[1]. Its aim was to summarise the most pressing actions required, in Butterfly Conservation's opinion, to tackle the decline of butterflies. We have revisited the 10-point plan here, almost exactly five years on, to give our view of the progress achieved and to highlight the urgent need for further action.

1. Agricultural reform

The EU Common Agricultural Policy (CAP) has been reformed, resulting in a modest switch away from payments solely for production to more support for environmentally sensitive farming. Cross compliance has been introduced, linking the payment of agricultural subsidies to good agricultural and environmental practice. The pace of reform is slow, however, and some production subsidies are still driving habitat destruction and hindering restoration. The UK and Republic of Ireland have introduced a range of new "green farming schemes", normally referred to as agri-environment schemes, some of which have been shown already to benefit target butterfly species and other wildlife[2]. Some of the new schemes are more flexible and include promising new measures that should help butterflies (e.g. the Environmental Stewardship Scheme in England). Continued development and targeting of schemes and careful monitoring of their outcomes would improve the prospects still further. The remaining (major) problems are that these schemes are poorly funded compared with production subsidies and that some of them are not well targeted for biodiversity. There is also some doubt about future budgets for rural development schemes and, therefore, further reform of the CAP is needed urgently. The new UKBMS provides a valuable method of monitoring the effectiveness of new farming schemes and it is hoped that butterflies will be adopted as a key indicator of the success of agricultural reform.

Our verdict on progress: 6/10

2. Implementation of national Biodiversity Action Plans

The UK and Irish Governments have made an ambitious commitment under the Göteborg Protocol and the Kyiv Biodiversity Resolution to halt the loss of biodiversity in Europe by 2010. The resulting Countdown 2010 initiative will give a clear focus for activity over the next five years. The UK Biodiversity Action Plan (BAP) is being implemented and has already brought substantial benefits for threatened butterflies[3]. The species afforded priority status in the plan are currently being reviewed and many additional butterflies have been proposed using evidence from the BNM and UKBMS data. National plans and priorities are being developed for the UK countries (e.g. Northern Ireland has listed five butterflies as Priority Species). The Republic of Ireland has produced a National Biodiversity Plan and all-Ireland action plans have been developed for four species so far, though none of them are for butterflies or other invertebrates. The BAP process has played a significant role in raising awareness of the conservation needs of butterflies and other groups (e.g. the importance of open woodland for the Pearl-bordered Fritillary in Scotland). The initiative can take credit for the significant recovery of some priority butterflies in the UK, notably the Large Blue, and the regional recovery of the Heath Fritillary and High Brown Fritillary. However, other Priority Species continue to decline and resources have fallen far short of those needed for full implementation of all species action plans. The proposed addition of further butterflies to the UK BAP list will require the redirection of effort and considerable additional investment if the success of the process is to be maintained.

Our verdict on progress: 6/10

1 Asher *et al.* 2001
2 For example, see www.defra.gov.uk/erdp, www.ruralni.gov.uk/environment/countryside/, www.scotland.gov.uk/Topics/Agriculture/grants/Schemes/Intro, www.ccw.gov.uk/generalinfo/index.cfm?Subject=Agriculture&lang=en, and www.agriculture.gov.ie/index.jsp?file=schemes/reps_cover.xml
3 www.ukbap.org.uk

3. Strengthening of wildlife law

The law protecting wildlife and special sites has been strengthened considerably in each of the devolved countries within the UK and new measures have been introduced to ensure that habitats can be managed effectively[4]. Many important butterfly areas are not designated as special sites and therefore do not benefit from these advances. However, they should benefit from other measures (see Points 1 and 4) and could be afforded better protection through the new planning system (see Point 5). The legislation that affords strict protection to listed species (which include five butterflies) has also been strengthened and gives additional protection for existing breeding areas. Further measures are needed to safeguard habitats in and around existing colonies, which are not covered by existing legislation, but which may be vital for long-term persistence of the species.

Our verdict on progress: 8/10

4. Encouraging woodland biodiversity

Forestry grants have been revised in some countries to give greater priority to conservation and better targeting of threatened species and habitats. The Forestry Commission is also implementing positive management for butterflies in many of its forests in Britain, guided by a specific action plan for butterflies. Funding and grants for positive management of ancient woodland are still very limited, however, and butterflies continue to decline, mainly because of low levels of management. It is also clear that the rise in deer numbers is a growing problem for some butterfly species. The development of biofuels could benefit biodiversity if it stimulates active woodland management, but not if it simply results in monocultures of fast-growing willows.

Our verdict on progress: 4/10

5. Promotion of sustainable development

Important new legislation has been introduced in the UK that places sustainable development at the heart of the planning system. The Nature Conservation (Scotland) Act 2004 placed a duty on all public bodies to further nature conservation. In England, new Planning Policy Statements (PPS 1 and 9) state clearly that the Government's objectives for planning are to promote sustainable development and to conserve, enhance **and restore** the diversity of England's wildlife[5]. Any harm to wildlife must now be first mitigated wherever possible or, if damage is unavoidable, appropriate compensation must be provided (e.g. habitat restoration elsewhere). Under the new guidance, planning permission could be refused if harm cannot be prevented, mitigated or compensated. Moreover, planning decisions should be based upon up-to-date information on the biodiversity of the area, giving a clear role for the BNM data summarised in this book. However, it remains to be seen how well these policies are implemented in practice and how they will be reconciled with competing policies and growing development pressure. As with other policies, butterflies provide valuable indicators of sustainable development and the effectiveness of such legislation and guidance.

Our verdict on progress: 7/10

6. Protection of important butterfly sites

Very few additional important butterfly sites have been protected by new designations in the last five years and many are still highly vulnerable. However, many sites are now being listed as County Wildlife Sites and could benefit from measures described under other points. A large number of Special Areas for Conservation (SACs) have been designated under the EU Habitats and Species Directive, many of them covering habitats for threatened butterflies, but most of these were already Sites of Special Scientific Interest. Nevertheless, SAC designation has strengthened the protection of these sites

4   For example, see www.defra.gov.uk/
    wildlife%2Dcountryside/cl/ and
    www.opsi.gov.uk/legislation/scotland/acts2004/
    20040006.htm
5   www.odpm.gov.uk/index.asp?id=1164839,
    www.odpm.gov.uk/index.asp?id=1148207

considerably. In addition, several new SACs have been designated specifically for the Marsh Fritillary (our only resident butterfly listed on Annexe 2 of the Directive), though these are far from comprehensive and it is difficult to see how they will achieve the required Favourable Conservation Status for the species without further strong measures being enforced. In Wales, SACs have been designated to cover potential, as well as existing, breeding areas for the butterfly, which is an extremely positive step towards conserving viable metapopulations in the long term. We hope the latter is an example that other countries will follow and that the improved legislation and agricultural reform will help protect other key butterfly sites.

Our verdict on progress: 5/10

7. Restoring the landscape

Conservationists are placing far greater emphasis on landscape-scale projects, which aim to conserve biodiversity by restoring the links between fragmented habitats. Agri-environment schemes also have the potential to improve habitats on a landscape scale, if the actions they promote (e.g. reinstating hedgerows and field margins of native vegetation) are undertaken by enough landowners. It remains to be seen if this will be the case, but we are optimistic that the new Entry Level Environmental Stewardship scheme in England will help improve the quality of habitats in the wider countryside. However, there are fears that the broad schemes being developed in other countries may deliver little for biodiversity. All these schemes require increased funding and refinement in coming years if we are to restore a viable landscape for butterflies.

Our verdict on progress: 6/10

8. Development of research, survey and monitoring

A wealth of valuable research has been conducted over the past five years to help conserve threatened species more effectively, to monitor the benefits of habitat management and to predict the impacts of climate change. The UK Government has funded the development of the UK Butterfly Monitoring Scheme, a major new system for monitoring butterflies, including research to develop butterflies as indicators of environmental policy. It is hoped that a similar scheme might be developed in Ireland. The planned establishment of a National Biological Records Centre in the Republic of Ireland is a significant positive development. However, resources are still needed to continue the Butterflies for the New Millennium recording scheme to track changes into the future and to target conservation measures at the local scale.

Our verdict on progress: 6/10

9. Increasing awareness of the need for conservation

Butterflies now attract significantly more media attention than five years ago and the decline of butterflies has been widely reported. As a consequence, both the general public and policy makers are more aware of the fate of our butterflies and the threats they face. Measures to benefit butterflies have been incorporated into the design of new policies (e.g. the Environmental Stewardship agri-environment scheme), but there is more work to be done to widen awareness, for example of the importance of butterflies as indicators of a healthy environment.

Our verdict on progress: 6/10

10. Obtaining adequate funds for the above actions

Substantial funding for the above actions has been provided by the UK statutory conservation agencies and by charitable donations, but the magnitude of the problems outlined in this book show that far more resources are needed to address the steep decline of butterflies and other wildlife.

Our verdict on progress: 5/10

Appendix

Total numbers of 10km squares in which species were recorded in Britain, Isle of Man, Ireland and the Channel Islands.

Species	1970–82	1995–99	2000–04	1995–2004	Annual rate of population change Long-term	10-year (1995–2004)
Chequered Skipper	34	28	25	32	–	–
Small Skipper	1,098	1,464	1,420	1,549	–	–
Essex Skipper	303	645	650	723	–	–
Lulworth Skipper	13	12	13	13	-1.1%	6.7%
Silver-spotted Skipper	25	31	40	43	11.8% ***	0.2%
Large Skipper	1,246	1,586	1,434	1,648	0.4%	-5.2% *
Dingy Skipper	662	637	551	752	-1.6% **	-3.3%
Grizzled Skipper	419	386	319	426	-1.4%	-5.8%
Swallowtail	14	52	56	91	–	–
Wood White/Réal's Wood White	336	323	263	440	-3.7%	1.1%
Clouded Yellow	355	1,246	1,600	1,839	10.5%	39.3%
Brimstone	1,029	1,372	1,320	1,553	0.7%	-1.3%
Large White	2,402	2,792	2,541	3,059	-1.2%	1.8%
Small White	2,322	2,608	2,397	2,862	0.5%	-4.4%
Green-veined White	2,755	3,443	3,250	3,596	0.4%	0.8%
Orange-tip	1,838	2,743	2,558	3,062	0.7%	-0.9%
Green Hairstreak	773	1,046	1,009	1,373	-1.0%	-3.1%
Brown Hairstreak	189	149	125	174	–	–
Purple Hairstreak	608	1,030	856	1,183	1.5%	-2.8%
White-letter Hairstreak	471	578	507	754	-4.3% *	-10.5%
Black Hairstreak	26	25	24	29	–	–
Small Copper	2,005	2,349	2,224	2,688	-0.3%	-5.7%
Small Blue	264	305	271	376	-0.3%	9.2%
Silver-studded Blue	121	94	80	105	0.0%	-13.3% *
Brown Argus	379	729	691	850	0.5%	-9.8% *
Northern Brown Argus	68	121	126	158	-0.4%	-3.9%
Common Blue	2,277	2,668	2,492	3,025	0.3%	-2.6%
Chalkhill Blue	205	206	179	226	1.0%	-4.6%
Adonis Blue	88	96	92	113	1.0%	5.6%
Holly Blue	896	1,575	1,485	1,742	4.9%	-3.9%
Duke of Burgundy	126	108	74	117	-1.3%	-9.1% *
White Admiral	276	376	331	442	-3.4% **	-4.8%
Purple Emperor	75	90	79	112	-0.8%	3.2%
Red Admiral	1,842	2,896	2,838	3,244	5.5% ***	-5.2%
Painted Lady	1,427	2,488	2,793	3,112	6.7%	9.0%
Small Tortoiseshell	2,668	3,061	2,949	3,370	-0.6%	-4.5%
Peacock	1,890	2,670	2,809	3,144	2.3% **	-5.5%
Comma	888	1,516	1,559	1,674	5.1% ***	5.7%
Small Pearl-bordered Fritillary	674	774	533	879	-4.2% ***	-1.2%
Pearl-bordered Fritillary	386	269	157	294	-3.8% **	-7.6%
High Brown Fritillary	127	56	23	57	-0.5%	-18.8% *
Dark Green Fritillary	853	1,032	827	1,299	1.8%	-1.2%
Silver-washed Fritillary	591	667	615	860	1.0%	-1.7%
Marsh Fritillary	411	315	260	383	-6.0% **	6.3%
Glanville Fritillary	13	13	10	14	–	–
Heath Fritillary	17	13	11	14	-6.4% **	-6.6%
Speckled Wood	1,506	2,250	2,303	2,594	3.5% ***	5.8% *
Wall	1,707	1,686	1,488	1,925	-3.7% **	-0.2%
Mountain Ringlet	34	39	31	47	–	–
Scotch Argus	244	327	315	414	4.0% **	-0.1%
Marbled White	431	663	636	750	3.0% **	-1.8%
Grayling	730	738	581	893	-2.5% **	-5.7% **
Gatekeeper	1,192	1,477	1,461	1,561	-0.5%	-0.6%
Meadow Brown	2,695	3,108	3,090	3,466	0.9%	-0.5%
Ringlet	1,585	2,268	2,397	2,728	5.7% ***	3.3%
Small Heath	2,117	2,363	2,025	2,652	-2.6% **	-3.7%
Large Heath	334	392	332	542	-1.2%	5.2%

References

Aagaard, K., Hindar, K., Pullin, A.S., James, C.H., Hammarstedt, O., Balstad, T., Hanssen, O., 2002. Phylogenetic relationships in brown argus butterflies (Lepidoptera: Lycaenidae: *Aricia*) from northwestern Europe. *Biological Journal of the Linnean Society* **75**, 27–37.

Aldwell, B., 2003. A survey of local resident butterflies in County Donegal, Ireland. *Bulletin of the Irish Biogeographical Society* **27**, 202–226.

Aldwell, B., Nash D.W., 2005. The holly blue butterfly *Celastrina argiolus* (L.) in Co Dublin. *Irish Naturalists' Journal* **28**, 120–122.

Asher, J., Warren, M., Fox, R., Harding, P., Jeffcoate, G., Jeffcoate S., 2001. *The Millennium Atlas of Butterflies in Britain and Ireland*. Oxford University Press, Oxford.

Balmer, O., Erhardt, A., 2000. Consequences of succession on extensively grazed grasslands for central European butterfly communities: rethinking conservation practices. *Conservation Biology* **14**, 746–757.

Balmford, A., Bond, W., 2005. Trends in the state of nature and their implications for human well-being. *Ecology Letters* **8**, 1218–1234.

Beccaloni, G.W., Gaston, K.J., 1995. Predicting species richness of Neotropical forest butterflies: Ithomiinae (Lepidoptera: Nymphalidae) as indicators. *Biological Indicators* **71**, 77–86.

Benes, J., Kepka, P., Konvicka, M., 2003. Limestone quarries as refuges for European xerophilous butterflies. *Conservation Biology* **17**, 1058–1069.

Benton, T.G., Bryant, D.M., Cole, L., Crick, H.Q.P., 2002. Linking agricultural practice to insect and bird populations: a historical study over three decades. *Journal of Applied Ecology* **39**, 673–687.

Bergman, K-O., Kindvall, O., 2004. Population viability analysis of the butterfly *Lopinga achine* in a landscape in Sweden. *Ecography* **27**, 49–58.

Berry, P.M., Dawson, T.P., Harrison, P.A., Pearson, R.G., 2002. Modelling potential impacts of climate change on the bioclimatic envelope of species in Britain and Ireland. *Global Ecology and Biogeography* **11**, 453–462.

Bourn, N.A.D., Thomas, J.A., 2002. The challenge of conserving grassland insects at the margins of their range in Europe. *Biological Conservation* **104**, 285–292.

Bourn, N., Thomas, J., Stewart, K., Clarke, R., 2002. Importance of habitat quality and isolation: implications for the management of butterflies in fragmented landscapes. *British Wildlife* **13**, 398–403.

Bourn, N.A.D., McCracken, M.E., Wigglesworth, T., Brereton, T., Fox, R., Roy, D., Warren, M.S., 2005. *Proposed changes to the BAP Priority Species list: butterflies*. Butterfly Conservation Report SO5-23, Wareham.

Brereton, T., 2004. Farming and butterflies. *The Biologist* **51**, 32–36.

Brereton, T., 2006. Monitoring the Heath Fritillary *Mellicta athalia* at Thornden and West Blean Woods. In *Monitoring nature conservation in cultural landscapes: a practical guide and case studies*, (ed. C. Hurford, M. Schneider), pp. 271–284. Springer, Dordrecht.

Brereton, T., Greatorex-Davies, N., Fox, R., Roy, D., Stewart, K., Warren, M., 2003. *Annual monitoring coverage of conservation priority butterflies*. Butterfly Conservation Report SO3-11, Wareham.

Brereton, T., Wigglesworth, T., Warren, M.S., Stewart, K., 2005. *BD1446: Agri-environment schemes and butterflies: re-assessing the impacts and improving delivery of BAP targets*. Butterfly Conservation Final Project Report, supplied to Defra.

Brereton, T., Roy, D., Greatorex-Davies, N., 2006. Thirty years and counting. The contribution to conservation and ecology of butterfly-monitoring in the UK. *British Wildlife* **17**, 162–170.

Brown, K.S., 1991. Conservation of neotropical environments: insects as indicators. In *The conservation of insects and their habitats*, (ed. N.M. Collins, J.A. Thomas), pp. 350–404. Academic Press, London.

Brown, K.S., Freitas, A.V.L., 2000. Atlantic forest butterflies: indicators for landscape conservation. *Biotropica* **32**, 934–956.

Bryant, S.R., Thomas, C.D., Bale, J.S., 2002. The influence of thermal ecology on the distribution of three nymphalid butterflies. *Journal of Applied Ecology* **39**, 43–55.

Buglife, 2004. *UK Biodiversity Action Plan review. Stage 1: selecting potential priority species – guidance for non-marine invertebrates*. Buglife, Peterborough.

Bulman, C.R., 2001. *Conservation biology of the Marsh Fritillary butterfly Euphydryas aurinia*. Unpublished Ph.D. thesis, University of Leeds.

Bulman, C., 2004. The Heath Fritillary. *Butterfly* **87**, 21–23.

Bulman, C.R., 2005. Plain success for Marsh Fritillary. *Butterfly* **89**, 16.

Burke, S., Pullin, A.S., Wilson, R.J., Thomas, C.D., 2005. Selection for discontinuous life-history traits along a continuous thermal gradient in the butterfly *Aricia agestis*. *Ecological Entomology* **30**, 613–619.

Burton, J.F., 2001. The responses of European insects to climate change. *British Wildlife* **12**, 188–198.

Collins, N.M., Thomas, J.A., 1991. *The conservation of insects and their habitats*. Academic Press, London.

Conrad, K.F., Warren, M., Fox, R., Parsons, M., Woiwod, I.P., in press. Rapid declines of common, widespread British moths provide evidence of an insect biodiversity crisis. *Biological Conservation*.

Cowley, M.J.R., Thomas, C.D., Thomas, J.A., Warren, M.S., 1999. Flight areas of British butterflies: assessing species status and decline. *Proceedings of the Royal Society B* **266**, 1587–1592.

Critchley, C.N.R., Burke, M.J.W., Stevens, D.P., 2004. Conservation of lowland semi-natural grasslands in the UK: a review of botanical monitoring results from agri-environment schemes. *Biological Conservation* **115**, 263–278.

Crozier, L., 2003. Winter warming facilitates range expansion: cold tolerance of the butterfly *Atalopedes campestris*. *Oecologia* **135**, 648–656.

Davis, S., Corbett, S., 2004. The natural history and conservation of Porton Down. *British Wildlife* **15**, 381–390.

Davies, H., 2005. *The consequences of positive management of protected areas to achieve Government targets – how threatened UK butterflies are faring*. Unpublished M.Sc. thesis, University of Oxford.

Davies, Z.G., Wilson, R.J., Brereton, T.M., Thomas, C.D., 2005. The re-expansion and improving status of the silver-spotted skipper butterfly (*Hesperia comma*) in Britain: a metapopulation success story. *Biological Conservation* **124**, 189–198.

Davies, Z.G., Wilson, R.J., Coles, S., Thomas, C.D., 2006. Changing habitat associations of a thermally constrained species, the silver-spotted skipper butterfly, in response to climate warming. *Journal of Animal Ecology* **75**, 247–256.

de Heer, M., Kapos, V., ten Brink, B.J.E., 2005. Biodiversity trends in Europe: development and testing of a species trend indicator for evaluating progress towards the 2010 target. *Philosophical Transactions of the Royal Society B* **360**, 297–308.

Defra, 2002. *Working with the grain of nature – a biodiversity strategy for England*. Department for Environment, Food and Rural Affairs, London.

Dell, D., Sparks, T.H., Dennis, R.L.H., 2005. Climate change and the effect of increasing spring temperatures on emergence dates of the butterfly *Apatura iris* (Lepidoptera: Nymphalidae). *European Journal of Entomology* **102**, 161–167.

Dennis, R.L.H., 1993. *Butterflies and climate change*. Manchester University Press, Manchester.

Dennis, R.L.H., 2001. Progressive bias in species status is symptomatic of fine-grained mapping units subject to repeated sampling. *Biodiversity and Conservation* **10**, 483–494.

Dennis, R.L.H., Eales, H.T., 1997. Patch occupancy in *Coenonympha tullia* (Müller, 1764) (Lepidoptera: Satyrinae): habitat quality matters as much as patch size and isolation. *Journal of Insect Conservation* **1**, 167–176.

Dennis, R.L.H., Sparks, T.H., 2006. When is a habitat not a habitat? Dramatic resource use changes under differing weather conditions for the butterfly *Plebejus argus*. *Biological Conservation* **129**, 291–301.

Dennis, R.L.H., Thomas, C.D., 2000. Bias in butterfly distribution maps: the influence of hot spots and access. *Journal of Insect Conservation* **4**, 73–77.

Dennis, R.L.H., Sparks, T.H., Hardy, P.B., 1999. Bias in butterfly distribution maps: the effects of sampling effort. *Journal of Insect Conservation* **3**, 33–42.

Dennis, R.L.H., Shreeve, T.G., Van Dyck, H., 2003. Towards a functional resource-concept for habitat: a butterfly biology viewpoint. *Oikos* **102**, 417–426.

Dennis, R.L.H., Hodgson, J.G., Grenyer, R., Shreeve, T.G., Roy, D.B., 2004. Host plants and butterfly biology. Do host-plant strategies drive butterfly status? *Ecological Entomology* **29**, 12–26.

Dennis, R.L.H., Shreeve, T.G., Isaac, N.J.B., Roy, D.B., Hardy, P.B., Fox, R., Asher, J., 2006a. The effects of visual apparency on bias in butterfly recording and monitoring. *Biological Conservation* **128**, 486–492.

Dennis, R.L.H., Stefanescu, C., Tremewan, W.G., 2006b. Why does *Vanessa atalanta* (Linnaeus) (Lepidoptera: Nymphalidae) engage in late summer territorial disputes when close relatives are feeding up for overwintering? *Entomologist's Gazette* **57**, 83–89.

Department of Arts, Heritage, Gaeltacht and the Islands, 2002. *National biodiversity plan*. Department of Arts, Heritage, Gaeltacht and the Islands, Dublin.

Donald, P.F., Evans, A.D., 2006. Habitat connectivity and matrix restoration: the wider implications of agri-environment schemes. *Journal of Applied Ecology* **43**, 209–218.

Ecoscope/CPM/CJC Consulting, 2003. *Review of agri-environment schemes – monitoring and R&D results*. Ecoscope/CPM/CJC Consulting Final Report, supplied to Defra.

Ehrlich, P.R., 1994. Energy use and biodiversity loss. *Philosophical Transactions of the Royal Society B* **344**, 99–104.

Ellis, S., 2003. Habitat quality and management for the northern brown argus butterfly *Aricia artaxerxes* in North East England. *Biological Conservation* **113**, 285–294.

Emmet, A.M., 1989. The vernacular names and early history of British butterflies. In *The moths and butterflies of Great Britain and Ireland, 7, part 1, Hesperiidae–Nymphalidae, the butterflies*, (ed. A.M. Emmet, J. Heath), pp. 7–21. Harley Books, Colchester.

Emmet, A.M., Heath, J., 1990. *The moths and butterflies of Great Britain and Ireland, 7, part 1, Hesperiidae–Nymphalidae, the butterflies*. Harley Books, Colchester. (Paperback edition revised with minor corrections).

Fleishman, E., Ray, C., Sjögren-Gulve, P., Boggs, C.L., Murphy, D.D., 2002. Assessing the role of patch quality, area, and isolation in predicting metapopulation dynamics. *Conservation Biology* **16**, 706–716.

Fleishman, E., Thomson, J.R., Mac Nally, R., Murphy, D.D., Fay, J.P., 2005. Using indicator species to predict richness of multiple taxonomic groups. *Conservation Biology* **19**, 1125–1137.

Forister, M.L., Shapiro, A.M., 2003. Climatic trends and advancing spring flight of butterflies in lowland California. *Global Change Biology* **9**, 1130–1135.

Fowles, A.P., Smith, R.G., 2006. Mapping the habitat quality of patch networks for the marsh fritillary *Euphydryas aurinia* (Rottemburg, 1775) (Lepidoptera, Nymphalidae) in Wales. *Journal of Insect Conservation* **10**, 161–177.

Fox, R., 2001. Butterflies and moths. In *The changing wildlife of Great Britain and Ireland*, (ed. D.L. Hawksworth), pp. 300–327. Taylor and Francis, London.

Fox, R., 2002. Is the grass always greener in the green belt? *Butterfly Conservation News* **79**, 2–5.

Fox, R., Williams, L., 2006. A commentary on recent changes to butterfly distributions in the London area. *Entomologist's Record and Journal of Variation* **118**, 69–84.

Fox, R., Warren, M., Asher, J., Jeffcoate, G., Jeffcoate, S., Harding, P., 2001a. Migrant butterflies and the Millennium Atlas. *Entomologist's Record and Journal of Variation* **113**, 103–112.

Fox, R., Warren, M., Asher, J., Harding, P., Jeffcoate, G., Jeffcoate, S., 2001b. Expanding butterfly distributions, climate change and the Millennium Atlas. *Atropos* **13**, 17–23.

Franco, A.M.A., Hill, J.K., Kitschke, C., Collingham, Y.C., Roy, D.B., Fox, R., Huntley, B., Thomas, C.D., in press. Impacts of climate warming and habitat loss on extinctions at species' low-latitude range boundaries. *Global Change Biology*.

Freese, A., Fiedler, K., 2002. Experimental evidence for specific distinctness of the two wood white butterfly taxa, *Leptidea sinapis* and *L. reali* (Pieridae). *Nota Lepidopterologica* **25**, 39–59.

Gibson, C.W.D., 1998. *Brownfield: red data. The values artificial habitats have for uncommon invertebrates*. English Nature Research Report 273, Peterborough.

Grill, A., Knoflach, B., Cleary, D.F.R., Kati, V., 2005. Butterfly, spider, and plant communities in different land-use types in Sardinia, Italy. *Biodiversity and Conservation* **14**, 1281–1300.

Grime, J.P., Hodgson, J.G., Hunt, R., 1988. *Comparative plant ecology. A functional approach to common British species*. Unwin-Hyman, London.

Gutiérrez, D., 2005. Effectiveness of existing reserves in the long-term protection of a regionally rare butterfly. *Conservation Biology* **19**, 1586–1597.

Hanski, I., 1999. *Metapopulation ecology*. Oxford University Press, Oxford.

Hanski, I., 2003. Biology of extinctions in butterfly metapopulations. In *Butterflies – ecology and evolution taking flight*, (ed. C.L. Boggs, W.B. Watt, P.R. Ehrlich), pp. 577–602. University of Chicago Press, Chicago.

Hardy, P.B., Dennis, R.L.H., 1999. The impact of urban development on butterflies within a city region. *Biodiversity and Conservation* **8**, 1261–1279.

Heal, H., 1965. The Wood White *Leptidea sinapis* and the railways. *Irish Naturalists' Journal* **15**, 8–13.

Heath, J., Pollard, E., Thomas, J.A., 1984. *Atlas of butterflies in Britain and Ireland*. Viking, Harmondsworth.

Hickling, R., Roy, D.B., Hill, J.K., Fox, R., Thomas, C.D., 2006. The distributions of a wide range of taxonomic groups are expanding polewards. *Global Change Biology* **12**, 450–455.

Hill, J.K., Thomas, C.D., Lewis, O.T., 1996. Effects of habitat patch size and isolation on dispersal by *Hesperia comma* butterflies: implications for metapopulation structure. *Journal of Animal Ecology* **65**, 725–735.

Hill, J.K., Thomas, C.D., Huntley, B., 1999. Climate and habitat availability determine 20th century changes in a butterfly's range margins. *Proceedings of the Royal Society B* **266**, 1197–1206.

Hill, J.K., Collingham, Y.C., Thomas, C.D., Blakeley, D.S., Fox, R., Moss, D., Huntley, B., 2001. Impacts of landscape structure on butterfly range expansion. *Ecology Letters* **4**, 313–321.

Hill, J.K., Thomas, C.D., Fox, R., Telfer, M.G., Willis, S.G., Asher, J., Huntley, B., 2002. Responses of butterflies to 20th century climate warming: implications for future ranges. *Proceedings of the Royal Society B* **269**, 2163–2171.

Hilty, J., Merenlender, A., 2000. Faunal indicator taxa selection for monitoring ecosystem health. *Biological Conservation* **92**, 185–197.

Hoare, D., 2006. *Status of the Pearl-bordered Fritillary in England and Wales 2004*. Butterfly Conservation Report S06-03, Wareham.

Hobson, R., Bourn, N., Warren, M., 2002. Conserving the Marsh Fritillary in Britain. *British Wildlife* **13**, 404–411.

Hodges, S., 2005. *Species report – Black Hairstreak monitoring*. Unpublished report from Upper Thames Branch of Butterfly Conservation available from www.upperthamesbutterflies.co.uk

Holloway, G.J., Griffiths, G.H., Richardson, P., 2003. Conservation strategy maps: a tool to facilitate biodiversity action planning illustrated using the heath fritillary butterfly. *Journal of Applied Ecology* **40**, 413–421.

IPCC, 2001. *Climate change 2001: the scientific basis*. Cambridge University Press, Cambridge.

Jeffcoate, S., 2006. Seasonal variation in the use of vegetation resources by *Leptidea sinapis* (Linnaeus, 1758) (Lepidoptera: Pieridae), a multivoltine species in southern Britain: implications for its conservation at the edge of its range and in the context of climate change. *Entomologist's Gazette* **57**, 69–82.

Kerr, J.T., Sugar, A., Packer, L., 2000. Indicator taxa, rapid biodiversity assessment, and nestedness in an endangered ecosystem. *Conservation Biology* **14**, 1726–1734.

Key, R., 2000. Bare ground and the conservation of invertebrates. *British Wildlife* **11**, 183–191.

King, D., 2005. Climate change: the science and the policy. *Journal of Applied Ecology* **42**, 779–783.

Kirkland, P., 2005. The Scotch Argus. *Butterfly* **89**, 23–25.

Kleijn, D., Sutherland, W.J., 2003. How effective are European agri-environment schemes in conserving and promoting biodiversity? *Journal of Applied Ecology* **40**, 947–969.

Kleijn, D., Baquero, R.A., Clough, Y., Dýaz, M., De Esteban, J., Fernández, F., Gabriel, D., Herzog, F., Holzschuh, A., Jöhl, R., Knop, E., Kruess, A., Marshall, E.J.P., Steffan-Dewenter, I., Tscharntke, T., Verhulst, J., West, T.M., Yela, J.L., 2006. Mixed biodiversity benefits of agri-environment schemes in five European countries. *Ecology Letters* **9**, 243–254.

Knop, E., Kleijn, D., Herzog, F., Schmid, B., 2006. Effectiveness of the Swiss agri-environment scheme in promoting biodiversity. *Journal of Applied Ecology* **43**, 120–127.

Konvicka, M., Maradova, M., Benes, J., Fric, Z., Kepka, P., 2003. Uphill shifts in distribution of butterflies in the Czech Republic: effects of changing climate detected on a regional scale. *Global Ecology and Biogeography* **12**, 403–410.

Konvicka, M., Fric, Z., Benes, J., 2006. Butterfly extinctions in European states: do socio-economic conditions matter more than physical geography? *Global Ecology and Biogeography* **15**, 82–92.

Krauss, J., Steffan-Dewenter, I., Tscharntke, T., 2004. Landscape occupancy and local population size depends on host plant distribution in the butterfly *Cupido minimus*. *Biological Conservation* **120**, 355–361.

Krauss, J., Steffan-Dewenter, I., Muller, C.B., Tscharntke, T., 2005. Relative importance of resource quantity, isolation and habitat quality for landscape distribution of a monophagous butterfly. *Ecography* **28**, 465–474.

Kremen, C., Lees, D.C., Fay, J.P., 2003. Butterflies and conservation planning in Madagascar: from pattern to practice. In: *Butterflies – ecology and evolution taking flight*, (ed. C.L. Boggs, W.B. Watt, P.R. Ehrlich), pp. 517–540. University of Chicago Press, Chicago.

León-Cortés, J.L., Lennon, J., Thomas, C.D., 2003. Ecological dynamics of extinct species in empty habitat networks. 1. The role of habitat pattern and quality, stochasticity and dispersal. *Oikos* **102**, 449–464.

Lunn, J., 2001. Wildlife and mining in the Yorkshire coalfield. *British Wildlife* **12**, 318–326.

Maes, D., Van Dyck, H., 2001. Butterfly diversity loss in Flanders (North Belgium): Europe's worst case scenario? *Biological Conservation* **99**, 263–276.

Maes, D., Van Dyck, H., 2005. Habitat quality and biodiversity indicator performances of a threatened butterfly versus a multispecies group for wet heathlands in Belgium. *Biological Conservation* **123**, 177–187.

Maes, D., Bauwens, D., de Bruyn, L., Anselin, A., Vermeersch, G., van Landuyt, W., de Knijf, G., Gilbert, M., 2005. Species richness coincidence: conservation strategies based on predictive modelling. *Biodiversity and Conservation* **14**, 1345–1364.

Marren, P., 1998. A short history of butterfly-collecting in Britain. *British Wildlife* **9**, 362–370.

McCarty, J.P., 2001. Ecological consequences of recent climate change. *Conservation Biology* **15**, 320–331.

McCracken, M., Bulman, C., Borsje, A., Bourn, N., 2005. *Update: status of the Heath Fritillary Melitaea athalia on Exmoor in 2004 and 2005*. Butterfly Conservation Report SO5–28, Wareham.

McKernan, P., 2004. AONBs in the South East: landscape-scale action for woodland fritillary butterflies. In *Landscape ecology of trees and forests*, (ed. R. Smithers), pp. 232–239. International Association for Landscape Ecology (UK).

McLaughlin, J.F., Hellmann, J.J., Boggs, C.L., Ehrlich, P.R., 2002. Climate change hastens population extinctions. *Proceedings of the National Academy of Sciences* **99**, 6070–6074.

Menéndez, R., González-Megías, A., Hill, J.K., Braschler, B., Willis, S.G., Collingham, Y., Fox, R., Roy, D.B., Thomas, C.D., in press. Species richness changes lag behind climate change. *Proceedings of the Royal Society B*.

Middleton, P., 2000. The wildlife significance of a former colliery site in Yorkshire. *British Wildlife* **11**, 333–339.

Moilanen, A., Franco, A.M.A., Early, R.I., Fox, R., Wintle, B., Thomas, C.D., 2005. Prioritizing multiple-use landscapes for conservation: methods for large multi-species planning problems. *Proceedings of the Royal Society B* **272**, 1885–1891.

Nelson, B., Hughes, M., Nash, R., Warren, M., 2001. *Leptidea reali* Reissinger 1989 (Lep.: Pieridae): a butterfly new to Britain and Ireland. *Entomologist's Record and Journal of Variation* **113**, 97–102.

Oates, M., 2000. The Duke of Burgundy – conserving the intractable. *British Wildlife* **11**, 250–257.

Oates, M., Goodyear, L., Middleton, A., Willmott, K., 2005. *Purple Emperor 'master tree' project progress report 2004*. Unpublished report available from www.butterfly-conservation.org/species

Öckinger, E., Hammarstedt, O., Nilsson, S.G., Smith, H.G., 2006. The relationship between local extinctions of grassland butterflies and increased soil nitrogen levels. *Biological Conservation* **128**, 564–573.

Oostermeijer, J.G.B., van Swaay, C.A.M., 1998. The relationship between butterflies and environmental indicator values: a tool for conservation in a changing landscape. *Biological Conservation* **86**, 271–280.

Ovenden G.N., Swash A.R.H., Smallshire, D., 1998. Agri-environment schemes and their contribution to the conservation of biodiversity in England. *Journal of Applied Ecology* **35**, 955–960.

Pannekoek, J., van Strien, A., 1996. *TRIM (TRends & Indices for Monitoring data)*. Statistics Netherlands, Voorburg.

Parmesan, C., 1996. Climate and species' range. *Nature* **382**, 765–766.

Parmesan, C., 2003. Butterflies as bioindicators for climate change effects. In *Butterflies – ecology and evolution taking flight*, (ed. C.L. Boggs, W.B. Watt, P.R. Ehrlich), pp. 541–560. University of Chicago Press, Chicago.

Parmesan, C., Yohe, G., 2003. A globally coherent fingerprint of climate change impacts across natural systems. *Nature* **421**, 37–42.

Parmesan, C., Ryrholm, N., Stefanescu, C., Hill, J.K., Thomas, C.D., Descimon, H., Huntley, B., Kaila, L., Kullberg, J., Tammaru, T., Tennant, J., Thomas, J.A., Warren, M., 1999. Polewards shifts in geographical ranges of butterfly species associated with regional warming. *Nature* **399**, 579–583.

Peach, W.J., Lovett, L.J., Wotton, S.R., Jeffs, C., 2001. Countryside stewardship delivers cirl buntings (*Emberiza cirlus*) in Devon, UK. *Biological Conservation* **101**, 361–373.

Pollard, E., 1988. Temperature, rainfall and butterfly numbers. *Journal of Applied Ecology* **25**, 819–828.

Pollard, E., Eversham, B.C., 1995. Butterfly monitoring 2 – interpreting the changes. In *Ecology and conservation of butterflies*, (ed. A.S. Pullin), pp. 23–36. Chapman & Hall, London.

Pollard, E., Yates, T.J., 1993. *Monitoring butterflies for ecology and conservation*. Chapman & Hall, London.

Pollard, E., Hall, M.L., Bibby, T.J., 1986. *Monitoring the abundance of butterflies 1976–1985*. Nature Conservancy Council, Peterborough.

Pollard, E., Moss, D., Yates, T.J., 1995. Population trends of common British butterflies at monitored sites. *Journal of Applied Ecology* **32**, 9–16.

Ricketts, T.H., Daily, G.C., Ehrlich, P.R., 2002. Does butterfly diversity predict moth diversity? Testing a popular indicator taxon at local scales. *Biological Conservation* **103**, 361–370.

Robinson, R.A., Sutherland, W.J., 2002. Post-war changes in arable farming and biodiversity in Great Britain. *Journal of Applied Ecology* **39**, 157–176.

Root, T.L., Price, J.T., Hall, K.R., Schneider, S.H., Rosenzweig, C., Pounds, J.A., 2003. Fingerprints of global warming on wild animals and plants. *Nature* **421,** 57–60.

Rothery, P., Roy, D.B., 2001. Application of generalized additive models to butterfly transect count data. *Journal of Applied Statistics* **28**, 897–909.

Roy, D.B., Sparks, T.H., 2000. Phenology of British butterflies and climate change. *Global Change Biology* **6**, 407–416.

Roy, D.B., Thomas, J.A., 2003. Seasonal variation in the niche, habitat availability and population fluctuations of a bivoltine thermophilous insect near its range margin. *Oecologia* **134**, 439–444.

Roy, D.B., Rothery, P., Moss, D., Pollard, E., Thomas, J.A., 2001. Butterfly numbers and weather: predicting historical trends in abundance and the future effects of climate change. *Journal of Animal Ecology* **70**, 201–217.

Salmon, M.A., 2000. *The Aurelian legacy – British butterflies and their collectors*. Harley Books, Colchester.

Sazer, D., 2004. Joining up the dots – conserving the marsh fritillary. *Natur Cymru* **13**, 9–12.

Schröter, D., Cramer, W., Leemans, R., Prentice, C., Araújo, M.B., Arnell, N.W., Bondeau, A., Bugmann, H., Carter, T.R., Gracia, C.A., de la Vega-Leinert, A.C., Erhard, M., Ewert, F., Glendining, M., House, J.I., Kankaanpää, S., Klein, R.J.T., Lavorel, S., Lindner, M., Metzger, M.J., Meyer, J., Mitchell, T.D., Reginster, I., Rounsevell, M., Sabaté, S., Sitch, S., Smith, B., Smith, J., Smith, P., Sykes, M.T., Thonicke, K., Thuiller, W., Tuck, G., Zaehle, S., Zierl, B., 2005. Ecosystem service supply and vulnerability to global change in Europe. *Science* **310**, 1333–1337.

Schtickzelle, N., Choutt, J., Goffart, P., Fichefet, V., Baguette, M., 2005. Metapopulation dynamics and conservation of the marsh fritillary butterfly: Population viability analysis and management options for a critically endangered species in Western Europe. *Biological Conservation* **126**, 569–581.

Shirt, D.B., 1987. *British red data books, number 2 insects*. Nature Conservancy Council, Peterborough.

Skelton, M., 2003. The Clouded Yellow in Bournemouth, 1998–2003. In *Hampshire and Isle of Wight butterfly and moth report 2003*, (ed. J.Taverner), pp. 15–18. Hampshire and Isle of Wight Branch of Butterfly Conservation.

Smallshire, D., Robertson, P., Thompson, P., 2004. Policy into practice: the development and delivery of agri-environment schemes and supporting advice in England. *Ibis* **146**, 250–258.

Smith, R.M., Thompson, K., Hodgson, J.G., Warren, P.H., Gaston, K.J., 2006. Urban domestic gardens (IX): Composition and richness of the vascular plant flora, and implications for native biodiversity. *Biological Conservation* **129**, 312–322.

Smith, R.M., Warren, P.H., Thompson, K., Gaston, K.J., in press. Urban domestic gardens (VI): environmental correlates of invertebrate species richness. *Biodiversity and Conservation.*

Sparks, T.H., Roy, D.B., Dennis, R.L.H., 2005. The influence of temperature on migration of Lepidoptera into Britain. *Global Change Biology* **11**, 507–514.

Stace, C., 1997. *New flora of the British Isles (second edition)*. Cambridge University Press, Cambridge.

Stefanescu, C., Herrando, S., Páramo, F., 2004. Butterfly species richness in the north-west Mediterranean Basin: the role of natural and human-induced factors. *Journal of Biogeography* **31**, 905–915.

Sutherland, W.J., Armstrong-Brown, S., Armsworth, P.R., Brereton, T., Brickland, J., Campbell, C.D., Chamberlain, D.E., Cooke, A.I., Dulvy, N.K., Dusic, N.R., Fitton, M., Freckleton, R.P., Godfray, H.C., Grout, N., Harvey, H.J., Hedley, C., Hopkins, J.J., Kift, N.B., Kirby, J., Kunin, W.E., MacDonald, D.W., Markee, B., Naura, M., Neale, A.R., Oliver, T., Osborn, D., Pullin, A.S., Shardlow, M.E.A., Showler, D.A., Smith, P.L., Smithers, R.J., Solandt, J-L., Spencer, J., Spray, C.J., Thomas, C.D., Thompson, J., Webb, S.E., Yalden, D.W., Watkinson, A.R., in press. The identification of one hundred ecological questions of high policy relevance in the UK. *Journal of Applied Ecology.*

ter Braak, C.J.F., van Strien, A.J., Meijer, R., Verstrael, T.J., 1994. Analysis of monitoring data with many missing values: which method? In *Bird Numbers 1992: distribution, monitoring and ecological aspects*, (ed. W. Hagemeijer, T. Verstrael), pp. 663–673. SOVON, Beek-Ubbergen.

Thomas, C.D., Abery, J.C.G., 1995. Estimating rates of butterfly decline from distribution maps: the effect of scale. *Biological Conservation* **73**, 59–65.

Thomas, C.D., Thomas, J.A., Warren, M.S., 1992. Distributions of occupied and vacant butterfly habitats in fragmented landscapes. *Oecologia* **92**, 563–567.

Thomas, C.D., Hill, J.K., Lewis, O.T., 1998. Evolutionary consequences of habitat fragmentation in a localized butterfly. *Journal of Animal Ecology* **67**, 485–497.

Thomas, C.D., Bodsworth, E.J., Wilson, R.J., Simmons, A.D., Davies, Z.G., Musche, M., Conradt, L., 2001a. Ecological and evolutionary processes at expanding range margins. *Nature* **411**, 577–581.

Thomas, C.D., Wilson, R.J., Lewis, O.T., 2001b. Short-term studies underestimate 30-generation changes in a butterfly metapopulation. *Proceedings of the Royal Society B* **269**, 563–569.

Thomas, C.D., Cameron, A., Green, R.E., Bakkenes, M., Beaumont, L.J., Collingham, Y.C., Erasmus, B.F.N., Ferreira de Siqueira, M., Grainger, A., Hannah, L., Hughes, L., Huntley, B., van Jaarsveld, A.S., Midgley, G.F., Miles, L., Ortega-Huerta, M.A., Peterson, A.T., Phillips, O.L., Williams, S.E., 2004. Extinction risk from climate change. *Nature* **427**, 145–148.

Thomas, J.A., 1995. Why small cold-blooded insects pose different conservation problems to birds in modern landscapes. *Ibis* **137**, 112–119.

Thomas, J.A., 2005. Monitoring change in the abundance and distribution of insects using butterflies and other indicator groups. *Philosophical Transactions of the Royal Society B* **360**, 339–357.

Thomas, J.A., Clarke, R.T., 2004. Extinction rates and butterflies. *Science* **305**, 1563–1564.

Thomas, J.A., Rose, R.J., Clarke, R.T., Thomas, C.D., Webb, N.R., 1999. Intraspecific variation in habitat availability among ectothermic animals near their climatic limits and their centres of range. *Functional Ecology* **13**, 55–64.

Thomas, J.A., Bourn, N.A.D., Clarke, R.T., Stewart, K.E., Simcox, D.J., Pearman, G.S., Curtis, R., Goodger, B., 2001. The quality and isolation of habitat patches both determine where butterflies persist in fragmented landscapes. *Proceedings of the Royal Society B* **268**, 1791–1796.

Thomas, J.A., Telfer, M.G., Roy, D.B., Preston, C.D., Greenwood, J.J.D., Asher, J., Fox, R., Clarke, R.T., Lawton, J.H., 2004. Comparative losses of British butterflies, birds, and plants and the global extinction crisis. *Science* **303**, 1879–1881.

Thompson, K., Austin, K.C., Smith, R.M., Warren, P.H., Angold, P.G., Gaston, K.J., 2003. Urban domestic gardens I: putting small-scale plant diversity in context. *Journal of Vegetation Science* **14**, 71–78.

UK Biodiversity Group, 1998. *Tranche 2 action plans. Volume 1 – vertebrates and vascular plants*. English Nature, Peterborough.

van Swaay, C., van Strien, A., 2005. Using butterfly monitoring data to develop a European grassland butterfly indicator. In *Studies on the ecology and conservation of butterflies in Europe*, (ed. E. Keuhn, J. Thomas, R. Feldmann, J. Settele), pp. 106–108. Pensoft Publishers, Sofia.

van Swaay, C., Warren, M.S., 1999. *Red data book of European butterflies (Rhopalocera)*, Nature and Environment, No. 99. Council of Europe, Strasbourg.

van Swaay, C., Warren, M., Loïs, G., 2006. Biotope use and trends of European butterflies. *Journal of Insect Conservation* **10**, 189–209.

Vickery, J.A., Bradbury, R.B., Henderson, I.G., Eaton, M.A., Grice, P.V., 2004. The role of agri-environment schemes and farm management practices in reversing the decline of farmland birds in England. *Biological Conservation* **119**, 19–39.

Wainwright, D., 2005. *Conserving the Dingy Skipper Erynnis tages butterfly in North East England*. Butterfly Conservation Report SO5-34, Wareham.

Wainwright, D., 2006. Dingy Skipper at risk as the North East develops. *Butterfly* **91**, 18.

Warren, M.S., 1992. The conservation of British butterflies. In *The ecology of butterflies in Britain*, (ed. R.L.H. Dennis), pp. 246–274. Oxford University Press, Oxford.

Warren, M.S., Thomas, C.D., Thomas, J.A., 1984. The status of the Heath Fritillary butterfly *Mellicta athalia* Rott. in Britain. *Biological Conservation* **29**, 287–305.

Warren, M.S., Barnett, L.K., Gibbons, D.W., Avery, M.I., 1997. Assessing national conservation priorities: an improved red list of British butterflies. *Biological Conservation* **82**, 317–328.

Warren, M.S., Hill, J.K., Thomas, J.A., Asher, J., Fox, R., Huntley, B., Roy, D.B., Telfer, M.G., Jeffcoate, S., Harding, P., Jeffcoate, G., Willis, S.G., Greatorex-Davies, J.N., Moss, D., Thomas, C.D., 2001a. Rapid responses of British butterflies to opposing forces of climate and habitat change. *Nature* **414**, 65–69.

Warren, M., Clarke, S., Currie, F., 2001b. The Coppice for Butterflies Challenge: a targeted grant scheme for threatened species. *British Wildlife* **13**, 21–28.

Wenzel, M., Schmitt, T., Weitzel, M., Seitz, A., 2006. The severe decline of butterflies on western German calcareous grasslands during the last 30 years: a conservation problem. *Biological Conservation* **128**, 542–552.

Wigglesworth, T., 2005. *Action for the Brown Hairstreak: sharing good practice*. Butterfly Conservation Report SO5–04, Wareham. Available from www.butterfly-conservation.org/conservation

Wigglesworth, T., Bourn, N., Brereton, T., Bulman, C., 2004. *Status of the Heath Fritillary in the Blean Woodlands 2004*. Butterfly Conservation Report SO4-25, Wareham.

Wigglesworth, T., Brereton, T., Roy, D., 2005. *Plan for regional development of the transect network*. Unpublished report to the UKBMS Steering Group.

Wilson, R.J., Ellis, S., Baker, J.S., Lineham, M.E., Whitehead, R.W., Thomas, C.D., 2002. Large-scale patterns of distribution and persistence at the range margins of a butterfly. *Ecology* **83**, 3357–3368.

Wilson, R.J., Thomas, C.D., Fox, R., Roy, D.B., Kunin, W.E., 2004. Spatial patterns in species distributions reveal biodiversity change. *Nature* **432**, 393–396.

Wilson, R.J., Gutiérrez, D., Gutiérrez, J., Martínez, D., Agudo, R., Monserrat, V.J., 2005. Changes to the elevational limits and extent of species ranges associated with climate change. *Ecology Letters* **8**, 1138–1146.

Wood, B.C., Pullin, A.S., 2002. Persistence of species in a fragmented urban landscape: the importance of dispersal ability and habitat availability for grassland butterflies. *Biodiversity and Conservation* **11**, 1451–1468.

Index to species accounts